CONTENTS

CW00406751

PLATES

Front Cover - The start of the Lyke Wake Walk at the Lyke Wake Stone just outside of Osmotherley Village.

The
Lyke Wake Walk
Guide

The Official Guidebook of
The New Lyke Wake Club

A 40 Mile Crossing of
The North York Moors
from Osmotherley to Ravenscar

An Essential Guide to Help you Complete
The Lyke Wake Walk

Brian Smailes

Brian Smailes

Holds the record for the fastest 4 and 5 continuous crossings of the Lyke Wake Walk over the North York Moors. He completed the 210miles over rough terrain on 5 crossings in June 1995 taking 85hours and 50minutes. In 2005 he completed his 50th crossing.

Brian lectures on outdoor pursuit courses and between these travels extensively on walking expeditions and projects around Great Britain.

Long distance running and canoeing are other sports he enjoys, completing 25 marathons and canoeing the Caledonian Canal 3 times.

In August 2003 Brian walked from John O'Groats to Lands End, completing it in 34 days. In August 2001 he cycled from Lands End to John O'Groats, a journey of over 900miles in 6days 13hours 18minutes. This involved carrying food, clothing and tent, and was completed without any support between both ends.

Having travelled extensively throughout the UK, Europe and the Caribbean, Brian has recently been writing international travel guides to enable the holidaymaker to access the world with ease and enjoy it as much as he does, visiting Peru to walk 'The Inca Trail' and Cuba.

Brian lives in Yorkshire and has walked the hills and dales throughout the county. In compiling this 2nd edition of The Lyke Wake Guide, the route still holds as much pleasure and mystery in walking it again as it did the first time he walked it.

Top Ten series

THE YORKSHIRE DALES TOP TEN
ISBN 0-9526900-5-5

THE DERBYSHIRE TOP TEN
ISBN 1-903568-03-X

Other books

THE SCOTTISH COAST TO COAST WALK
ISBN 0-9526900-8-X

17 WALKS IN GLEN NEVIS
ISBN 1-903568-05-6

THE COMPLETE ISLE OF WIGHT COASTAL FOOTPATH
ISBN 0-9526900-6-3

ISLE OF WIGHT, NORTH TO SOUTH – EAST TO WEST
ISBN1-903568-07-2

THE NATIONAL 3 PEAKS WALK
ISBN 1-903568-24-2

THE YORKSHIRE 3 PEAKS WALK
ISBN 1-903568-22-6

THE LANCASHIRE TRAIL
ISBN 1-903568-10-2

THE 1066 COUNTRY WALK
ISBN 1-903568-00-5

THE GREAT GLEN WAY
ISBN 1-903568-13-7

JOHN O'GROATS TO LANDS END (WALK)
ISBN 1-903568-18-8

SHORT WALKS IN THE LAKE DISTRICT
ISBN 1-903568-20-X

THE YORKSHIRE 3 PEAKS WALK SKETCH MAP & ROUTE GUIDE
ISBN 1-903568-24-4

WALK HADRIAN'S WALL
ISBN 1-903568-40-4

LANDS END TO JOHN O'GROATS (CYCLE GUIDE)
ISBN 1-903568-11-0

Tourist Guides

TOURIST GUIDE TO VARADERO, CUBA
ISBN 1-903568-08-0

EXPLORE—FORT WILLIAM & GLEN NEVIS AREA
ISBN 1-903568-25-0

THIS EDITION REVISED 2005. ISBN 1-903568-14-5
CHALLENGE PUBLICATIONS
7, EARLSMERE DRIVE, BARNSLEY. S71 5HH
www.chall-pub.co.uk

ACKNOWLEDGEMENTS

In publishing this 2nd edition of The Lyke Wake Walk I must thank the following people for their help and contribution: -

Pam Smailes for her help in preparation of the text.

Geoff Whittaker and Janet Young for Photographs.

The New Lyke Wake Club for information and support.

Brian Smailes has asserted his right to be identified as author of this work in accordance with the copyright act 1988. All rights reserved. No part of this publication may be reproduced, stored in a retrieval system or transmitted in any form, by photocopying or otherwise without prior permission of the publisher.
ISBN 1-903568-14-5
First Published 1994
Second Edition 2003
Revised 2004
Published by: - Challenge Publications, 7 Earlsmere Drive, Barnsley, S71 5HH

The information recorded in this book is believed by the author to be correct at publication. No liabilities can be accepted for any inaccuracies, which may be found. It is recommended that anyone using this book should refer to the relevant map in conjunction with the book and be experienced in map recognition and compass use.

The description or representation of a route used does not necessarily mean there is existence of a right of way.

THE NEW LYKE WAKE CLUB

This was formed on 8th May 2004 to take over from the 'old' Lyke Wake Club which would close down, officially from October 2005, and to preserve the traditions of the founder of the walk, Bill Cowley who died in 1994.

All existing dirgers are entitled to membership of the club and they especially welcome new dirgers, that is people who complete at least one crossing of this famous route as described herein. Those who do complete the walk can purchase a **newly designed range of souvenirs** which are: -
Condolence Cards @.50p new size
Supporters Cards @.50p
Club Badge metal pin @ £2.50 new size
Woven Cloth Badge @ £2.30
Car Stickers @ £1.25
Club Tie @ £9.95
Lyke Wake CD with 170 photos of the route @ £4.00
Further copies of this guide book @ £3.50
T-Shirt @ £8.99, state size S,M,L,EX
Polo shirt @ £12.99, state size S,M,L,EX
Desk Calendar @ £4.50 (2006)
All the above are available from Gerry Orchard, 4, Cavendish Grove, Hull Road, York, YO10 3ND Cheques payable to New Lyke Wake Club.

The club is run by a council (committee) whose members live principally in Yorkshire but is open to people from all around the country. The club is a non-profit making body whose stated objectives are: -
Promoting interest in the North Yorkshire Moors, their history and folklore.
Assisting in safeguarding the moorland environment.
Encouraging the sport of long distance walking and running.
Providing advice and fellowship for those taking part.

The club has social events which are often in the form of a festive wake. Further details of these, other news, events and more information on the club can be found on the
clubs official website : -   www.lykewake.org

Crossings can be reported to : - Gerry Orchard, General Secretary, New Lyke Wake Club, 4, Cavendish Grove, Hull Road, York, YO10 3ND
Crossings can be reported now by e-mail : - crossing.report@lykewake.org
Every person who completes the walk on foot within 24 hours is eligible for membership, which should be reported within 28 days. **There is no membership fee.** Female members are titled *Witch* and males are titled *Dirger*.

INTRODUCTION

The Lyke Wake Walk is a 40 mile crossing of the North York Moors from Osmotherley to Ravenscar. Official starting point is the Lyke Wake Stone, just past the reservoir on the outskirts of Osmotherley at G.R. 470994 and finishing at the Lyke Wake Stone on Beacon Howes at Ravenscar G.R. 971012.

This crossing is generally considered a hard walk and a challenge to most people. There are seven sections with checkpoints between. Each section presents a different challenge. The first two sections run concurrently with the Cleveland Way before the Lyke Wake turns off east along a disused railway track.

Each year thousands of people attempt this challenge. Those who prepare beforehand usually succeed, those who do not, suffer on route. This booklet is a plain speaking guide which should help everyone, particularly the novice walker who may be accepting a challenge for the first time. The walk for many is 40miles of pure sweat and toil but can be as easy or as hard as you make it.

All references to places and roads are taken from the Ordnance Survey maps of North York Moors - Eastern and Western areas No.OL26 and OL27 and it is strongly recommended these maps are used in conjunction with this guide.

Plate 1
Scarth Wood Moor at the beginning of the Lyke Wake Walk .
The hill in the background is Carlton Bank just before checkpoint 1.
Coalmire Plantation is in the centre.

WALK PREPARATION

When preparing for this walk there are a number of points to consider. Fitness is the most important factor. Past experience has shown that people who do some type of fitness training in preparation for this walk succeed, those who drive from A to B and do nothing energetic are more likely to struggle.

After taking hundreds of people across these moors over many years and discussing their training with them, I have reached the following conclusion which may help you decide which type of training to do.

* **Jogging** - without a doubt is the best training for this walk. Build up gradually over a period of time to a maximum of 7miles in one run.

* **Walking** - this should be done regularly and gradually over a two month period. Start with a short walk and increase over time to a 25mile walk the week before the event. This should prepare you adequately by toning up your leg muscles as well as bedding your new boots in.

* **Cycling, Swimming, Keep Fit** - are other types of workouts to help you get fit.

Suitable equipment is another factor which helps. This need not be expensive but should be adequate for the job in hand. Equipment will be discussed in the next chapter in more detail.

Training in the use of a compass and map reading would be an advantage. particularly if you are doing the walk on your own or in a small group with no experienced guide or support team.

Throughout this walk there are numerous paths, sheep tracks and farmers paths which the inexperienced walker could quite easily wander along. Many of the tracks run parallel for a time then gradually lead off in different directions, therefore basic training in compass use would help, especially in the event of bad weather.

The right type of food to give energy and goodness to the body both before and during the walk is essential. Generally food containing a high level of carbohydrates consumed the week before the walk and while walking would help in producing energy. High energy food such as rice, pasta, potato, banana and milk will all help to build up your energy reserves and enable you to carry on when the going gets tough.

While walking you may find that high energy carbohydrate tablet/sweets will help you maintain a constant supply of energy. These are obtainable from most shops.

Now you have prepared adequately and are fit to tackle this arduous course, the next chapter looks at the equipment you need to complement your preparation.

Plate 2
Near triangulation pillar on Carlton Bank, the hill in the background is Cringle Moor showing the clear path up to the top. To the left on the hill is the alternative route.

EQUIPMENT

There is a vast amount of equipment you could use for this type of event costing from pence to pounds. The following list has been compiled from walkers comments and from what is reasonable for a person to carry on this particular walk. The equipment should not prove too expensive and indeed many walkers will already have most of the items on this list. This is only a suggested list and you may wish to vary it to suit your individual requirements.

1   Maps - O.S. Explorer OL26 & OL27 North York Moors Eastern & Western areas
2   Walking/fell boots
3   Stockings/socks - at least 3 pairs
4   Gloves
5   Woollen hat
6   Thin warm jumpers - in layers
7   Loose fitting trousers/walking trousers - **not jeans**
8   Cagoul/anorak/overtrousers (waterproof)
9   Complete spare change of clothes
10 Extra jumper for cold weather
11 A pair of soft shoes/trainers for before and after the walk and to be carried in case of problems with boots while walking
12 Basic first aid kit including plasters for blisters and Vaseline for chafing
13 Small rucksack
14 Compass
15 Survival bag
16 Torch with spare batteries & bulb
17 Whistle
18 Talcum powder for feet
19 Money for telephone in case of emergency
20 Note paper/pen
21 Toilet paper
22 Plastic drinks bottle, not more than one litre (you have to carry it 40miles)
23 Glucose tablets/sweets
24 Camera

When considering your equipment it is advisable to travel to the start in some comfortable trainers or shoes then change into your boots at the start of the walk. This means you will only have your boots on for the 12 - 19 hours that it would normally take to complete the crossing.

A common problem with this walk is upper leg muscle stiffness. Many people are accustomed to wearing light shoes on their feet. They then put on a pair of heavy boots and expect to walk 40miles without the necessary training to tone and build up the upper leg muscles. Result is muscle stiffness and eventually the upper legs seize. Many people have this problem and have to either drop out on route or be closely supported to the nearest check point, so beware!

I was once given a useful tip regarding boots and the avoidance of blisters - boots need to be big enough to fit comfortably but not too big so your feet move around inside while walking. Remember to fit the boots with suitable socks before buying.

Sprinkle a liberal quantity of talcum powder on your feet and in the socks. Put talcum powder into your boots and on the outsides of your socks, then put your boots on making sure your feet fit snugly into them. This method has helped many people to keep their feet not only dry and fresh throughout but more importantly blister free after 42miles.

Remember to cut your toe nails short before you leave home so you don't get any undue pressure on your toes while walking, which will result in black toenails.

Walking in jeans is inadvisable for three reasons:-
1) When jeans get wet they are liable to rub and chafe the skin to the point where you can be extremely sore.
2) Wet jeans draw the body heat away which could leave you colder instead of warmer and may result in hypothermia.
3) Wet jeans are heavy and take a long time to dry.

Two extremely useful items are a pair of gloves and a woollen hat. Most heat is lost through the back of the head therefore it is prudent to carry a hat or balaclava to help retain your body heat especially in times of cold and wet weather. Because heat is also lost quickly from your extremities, gloves are a useful item to carry to help towards overall protection.

To combat erosion the advice of the North York Moors National Park is for groups to be small and not exceeding ten people

THE ROUTE

As stated earlier, this walk is divided into seven sections starting at the Lyke Wake Stone near Osmotherley. Time for this 1st section of 6miles is approx. 2hrs based on a total walking time of 13hrs not including stops at checkpoints.

Proceed up the hillside from the Lyke Wake Stone then turn right and easterly along the top continuing for a short distance *(plate 1)* until the path descends to meet the metalled road. Cross the road by the cattle grid and through the kissing gate there into the forest. Continue on the path for 500yds before bearing left to descend a steep path. At the bottom take your second turning right. Proceed for 600yds until you arrive at a stile on your left with a field beyond. Cross the field and stream at far side below then proceed up the metalled road to the telephone box at Huthwaite Green. Go through the gate to meet the challenge for this section 0.5mile further on this track. You arrive at the lower side of a wood.

Looking up, a set of stone steps rises steeply. These are at various heights and lengths. Because of the awkward and uneven step and the total number, together with the height climbed, most walkers feel temporarily exhausted on reaching the top. Although the steps help to combat erosion, they can be dangerous especially when wet or covered in moss.

After completing the steps challenge you leave the tree line with the wind probably getting stronger as you go through a gate to start the steady climb up Live Moor, on a stone slabbed path. This eventually leads up to the triangulation pillar on Carlton Bank. Height climbed is 1338ft. *(plate 2)*. Care needs to be taken especially on this first section while the body adapts to the conditions and changing temperature. More importantly can be the differences in weather, from no wind at the start to gale force winds at the summit on Carlton Bank with low cloud and extreme cold. The glider base at the top is a useful landmark but keep the path along the left side up to the triangulation pillar. Turn right and head down a path which is steep and rocky in places to arrive at checkpoint one, entrance to Carlton Bank Glider Club at the road crossing.

Near the minor road crossing at checkpoint one is the Lord Stones Cafe just round the bend. Excellent food and drinks are available during the daytime.

Section two of the walk takes approximately 1hr 30mins and is 4miles long. After leaving checkpoint one there are two directions you can take. The first takes you up a straight forward path which is very steep but leads you directly to the top of Drake Howe hill on Cringle Moor. Once on top there are excellent views up to 60miles on a clear day. Continue along the path on the top and down at the far side before proceeding along the right side of the forest known as Broughton Plantation.

The alternative route that can be used particularly in bad weather is a path around the left side of the the hill. This path is undulating with some water and springs appearing as you proceed around the side of the hill. Access is gained through a gate just up from the stone wall on the left near the foot of the hill. Whichever route you choose you will arrive at Broughton Plantation with a path along the right side of it.

On arriving at the forest go down a short steep ditch or dike beside two stone posts and back up the other side to cross a stile where the forest begins. Most walkers go this way though some prefer to traverse along the high, exposed peaks on your right. The track alongside the forest can be very wet and muddy with many stones interspersed along the route. Because there is a stone wall on one side and forest on the other, this stretch is generally quite sheltered. This section is usually considered a good toilet stop! Toilet stops are generally few and far between. Stay on this undulating track for 2miles.

Just before arriving at checkpoint two you descend a long steep hill called Hasty Bank where the path widens. Here you will see a seat on your right side. Bear right just past the seat, after reading the inscription on it, and go down the stone steps at the side of the wall to checkpoint two on Clay Bank Road.

Section three is the longest section and takes approximately 3hrs for this 10mile route. Cross the road and through a gate followed by a steep climb up the hill on Urra Moor to Botton Head, which is the highest point on the whole walk, 1490ft. On the top as you go through a gate the path is seen to be winding into the distance. Following this old path for 1.5miles leads you to the old railway line. When you see the railway line bear right on a narrow path leading up to the old railway line at a point called Bloworth Crossing, 1274ft.

This railway track is the main challenge in this section. Continue in an easterly direction on the flat track for 5miles. Just past Blakey Gill there is a short path off on your left up to the Lion Inn. Turn left on the road and head for Ralph Crosses T-junction where checkpoint three at Rosedale Head awaits you.

When walking on the old railway line it can be very windy as the wind sweeps up the valley and over the embankments. It would be advisable to carry suitable wind/ waterproof clothing while walking on this exposed track.

Prepare at checkpoint three for wet feet because the challenge in this next section is the peat bogs. This 5mile section usually takes around 2hrs to complete but wet or dry conditions can affect your travelling time by quite a lot. Turn right from Ralph Crosses and walk along the road towards Rosedale Abbey for nearly 2miles. This road is at least reasonably flat so gives the legs some relief. You pass a minor road on your left, then turn off left approximately 200yds further.

Cross the platform bridge over the roadside dike on to a well worn path. This can be difficult to find as you leave the road. Once over the brow of the hill and past the 'trig' point, you will be walking on thick peat. When dry you tend to bounce across, when wet you sink into it. There are natural springs which come to the surface so the ground is very wet in parts with reed beds and surface water or black wet peat where you can sink in sometimes when you least expect it. The path from leaving the road to checkpoint four at Shunner Howe is a direct straight line so not hard to follow except in fog or snow. Continue until you meet a road, where the checkpoint is nearby.

Experience has shown that to travel fairly light over this short section, if weather conditions permit, would help. The reason for this is because there are a number of dikes and ditches that you must cross. These are often full of water or unstable peat. To enable you to pass from one side to the other easier, leave heavy rucksacks and equipment with the back up team but retain waterproof and spare warm clothing with you. I must emphasis that this should only be done in times of good weather and with a reliable support team to meet you at checkpoint four.

The next section is approximately 8miles and takes around 2hrs 20mins for this demanding stretch from Shunner Howe to Eller Beck on the Pickering to Whitby road. Many people say this section is more than 9miles long. This is usually because they are often feeling stiff by this time and walking at a slower pace.

The challenge in this section is the steep ravine which the unsuspecting walker suddenly finds themselves at the top of. Before you arrive at the ravine you have, in parts, a difficult path to follow. When you leave Shunner Howe the path is quite well defined and can be wet and peaty for the first mile. Head for the high ground ahead called 'Blue Man i 'th' Moss' in a generally easterly direction. Once on the top the path then becomes very rock strewn and difficult to navigate over as well as being hard to follow. The narrow path swings right after passing the higher ground.

Wheeldale Plantation is approximately 500yds to your left. You will see the forest as you proceed along the rocky path but keep the forest line off to your left at a distance. The path continues to have many rocks on it until you cross Wheeldale Road and the terrain changes to more picturesque scenery. Cross a stile and proceed down the side of a farmers field that has been reclaimed from moorland. Here you cross the roman road and see the steep ravine you need to descend, to the beck near Wheeldale Lodge *(plate 3)*. While descending the hillside look across to see your path on the far side. Cross the stepping stones and ascend the other side on a steady climb to Simon Howe. At this point you may see checkpoint five ahead at Fylingdales and good views of all the surrounding area.

A long descent brings you to the railway line of the North York Moors Railway. You may even see the steam train on its regular journey from Grosmont to Pickering *(plate 4)*. Cross over the line and up the bank to checkpoint five at Eller Beck Bridge. There is only 8miles to complete now. It is advisable to consume food and drink quickly then continue before the legs become too stiff - time wasting at this stage could be critical!

Section five takes you across the road, which can be very busy. Follow a path from the far side of the stone bridge at the bend in the road for approx. 2.3miles. This leads along the side of Little Eller Beck (stream) and skirts around the military area of Fylingdales. Bear right onto a man made stony access road heading for the mound on the highest ground ahead (Lilla Howe), along the north-west side of the military area to just before Lilla Howe. Go through a 5 bar gate, new in 2003, on the military access road before crossing a short piece of sometimes boggy ground to arrive beside the stone cross on the top of Lilla Howe *(plate 5)*. At this point you have excellent views of the surrounding area, also of the mast which is at the finish.

The path gradually descends and after 2miles you again find yourself at the top of a ravine. This is Jugger Howe ravine which at the bottom is crossed by a narrow platform bridge *(plate 6)*, which in 2003 was in a state of disrepair. There is a steep ascent on the other side before it leads on to a gravel path then an old army road to checkpoint six, which is Jugger Howes at 630ft, near the Flask Inn on the Whitby/Scarborough road.

You will probably find at this stage that it is better to continue on to the finish rather than stop here for refreshnents and possibly seize up.

Cross the busy main A171 road with extreme care and up a short, steep embankment on to Stony Marl Moor, then it is a straight path in a north easterly direction for 2miles to finish at the Lyke Wake Stone at Beacon Howes 871ft. This will take approximately 30mins.

Celebrations are in order if you have enough energy, otherwise take a well earned rest!

'CONGRATULATIONS'

Plate 3
Looking down to Wheeldale Lodge & Wheeldale Beck

Plate 4
North York Moors Railway with Lyke Wake path crossing over,
just before checkpoint 5.

ON ROUTE ENCOUNTERS

Throughout the walk there are numerous items of interest. I will describe these in order of passing.

When starting near Osmotherley you will see the Lyke Wake Stone which is an awesome momento of what lies ahead.

Through the forest soon after starting you may see deer, fox, numerous rabbits and grouse. These animals have been sighted on many occasions.

On Carlton Bank 5.5miles into your journey there are excellent views from the top and along to the triangulation pillar. These include Bilsdale television booster mast which is a landmark to the south-east. Middlesborough and the Cleveland area can also be seen clearly from the top.

Even more awe inspiring are the views from the top of Drake Howe on Cringle Moor. At a height of 1427ft the panoramic view is spectacular. On a clear day Penshaw Monument near my home town of Sunderland can be seen over 60miles away to the north.

Proceeding towards checkpoint 2 you will pass a wooden seat near the end of the forest section. This has an inscription on it which you should read then proceed with vigour to the checkpoint!

Along the railway line 2.5miles past Bloworth crossing there is a small pile of limestone chippings. Just past here is a turning to the left down into Esklets on Westerdale Moor. This gives good viewing for those with time to spare and is in fact the old route of Lyke Wake Walk down into the valley and up Flat Howe to Ralph Crosses at Rosedale Head, checkpoint 3.

Near Ralph Crosses is an unusual boundry stone named White Cross, commonly known as Fat Betty, which you will see on route to the bog section. It forms part of the line of boundary stones but is individually distinctive.

Water, Water everywhere! Depending on the conditions and time of year you may find yourself up to the knees in black slimey peat or bouncing over it as you walk. Thankfully though over the last decade the boggy section between Ralph Crosses and Shunner Howe has dried considerably to what it was many years ago.

After passing several tumuli on your right, you arrive at Shunner Howe, checkpoint 4. On route to Eller Beck you can actually see the radio beacon at the finish near Ravenscar. This sighting may give inspirstion to those who may be 'struggling' at this stage.

A pleasant sight as you proceed is the scenery and the general area around the old roman road. This leads quickly down to Wheeldale Beck *(plate 3)*. Many people pause here for picnics and to bathe their feet in the beck near the stepping stones. A youth hostel nearby can make a good stopping point for the night for those with time to spare. Pre-book before you leave home. The village of Goathland, known to many as Aidensfield in Heartbeat, is barely 3miles from here.

When you make the long slow climb up towards the high ground and Simon Howe, 850ft, you will see the new Fylingdales military area from the top. The old 'golf balls' were removed in May 1994. Checkpoint 5 at Eller Beck is another popular place for picnics near the bridge but beware of the busy road.

Between checkpoints 5 & 6 is Lilla Howe. This is a raised earth mound on the hill and it supports a cross which is an early example of Christian Sculpture relating to Edwin, King of Northumbria in 633 AD *(plate 5)*.

On reaching this point there are good views of Beacon Howes, Scarborough and the sea. Grouse are often seen not only in this area but throughout the length of the walk.

Jugger Howe ravine is an intrepid sight from the top and sets a daunting task for any walker, located 1mile before checkpoint 6, to traverse both sides of this steep and potentially dangerous ravine and have the energy left to complete the last 3miles.

Eventually you arrive at the Lyke Wake Stone at Beacon Howes near Ravenscar. If you have enough energy, walk to your left of the radio beacon and look over the cliff. Good views of Robin Hoods Bay and the surrounding area can be seen from here.

Walkers may like to note that within 3miles of the finish there are some local public houses including the Flask Inn, Raven Hall Hotel and the Falcon Inn. The famous Smugglers Inn is only 0.5miles south of Beacon Howes for those in need of urgent refreshment!

Plate 5
The cross on Lilla Howe between checkpoints 5 & 6

Plate 6
Crossing Jugger Howe Beck just before checkpoint 6

SUPPORT TEAM

Most people usually attempt this walk from Osmotherley to Ravenscar with a support team who will meet them at each checkpoint and provide food and drinks. It is important to remember that if you are a walker you should keep in mind the distance between each checkpoint and the approximate time to complete the section. Consider your physical and mental state as you progress to each checkpoint and the weather conditions. You should then be able to decide whether you can continue to the next checkpoint or retire honourably at the one you are at.

A good support team who give verbal encouragement as well as hot food and drinks are essential for all walkers. When arriving at a checkpoint, walkers should not have to wait for food and drinks. These should be ready as the walkers arrive. Too long spent at a checkpoint will result in walkers feeling stiff and tired. As the walk progresses the time spent at a checkpoint becomes more critical as the body becomes stiffer.

Walkers should arrive at a checkpoint, be fed and watered and set off again within 15mins if possible.

A good safety precaution is for the backup team to operate a checking in system at each checkpoint. Walkers should report to their car or mini-bus driver at each checkpoint and be marked off on a walkers register. Taking this precaution should ensure no walker has gone astray between checkpoints.

All support teams must have an adequate supply of first aid equipment particularly adhesive plasters. They should also carry sleeping bags for any possible hypothermia cases and torches with spare batteries for any emergency at night.

Support teams should have one person who is familiar with the walk and understands the problems the walkers face in each section. There may be a need to go along the route to retrieve or assist a tired or injured walker. An emergency rucksack with the necessary equipment in should be ready. This pack should include some food and drink, note pad, pen, windproof, warm clothing and survival bag.

The success or failure of individuals or the whole group depends in some situations on how good the support team are overall and if they are at exactly the right place at the right time. This is sometimes a problem in thick fog! A good support team should have a responsible project leader who will have basic first aid skills and be a competent map reader.

SUPPORT PARTY ROUTE

From the car park. north for 2miles to A172, Turn right, after 2miles turn right and south-east through Carlton in Cleveland and up the hill, a total of 6miles.

CHECKPOINT ONE - CARLTON BANK

Top of the hill with small signpost 'CAFE' on left. Glider club entrance is on right side.

Continue on same road to B1257, at Chop Gate 4.2miles, turn left and head north to Hasty Bank a further 2.4miles.

CHECKPOINT TWO - HASTY BANK

Lay-by on both sides before the corner (trees on left). Steps down left side of forest. Gate on right side of road.

Continue north from lay-by and first turning right to Ingleby Greenhow 2miles, and Battersby 1.5miles and Kildale a further 2miles all in a north-easterly direction. 1.5miles after Kildale head south-east to Westerdale 3.5miles and a further 2.5miles to second car park.

CHECKPOINT THREE - RALPH CROSSES

Gravel car park on corner at the junction.

Head south east to Rosedale Abbey a distance of 5.5miles, turn left at public house in village and head north-east for 3miles.

CHECKPOINT FOUR - HAMER HOUSE

Old pits or tumulus then a wide path on left. Grass area near road also a few stones from ruins of Hamer House.

Continue north east for 6miles to Egton Bridge and east for 1.5miles to Grosmont, head east and then south-east for 2miles to A169, turn right and south for 4miles to checkpoint five.

CHECKPOINT FIVE - ELLER BECK

Lay - by on right just above bridge.

Head back north on same road towards Sleights and after 4.5miles turn right and east to Littlebeck, 1mile. Continue east to join B1416 after 1mile. Continue on this road and join A171. Turn right and head south for 3miles to checkpoint six.

CHECKPOINT SIX - JUGGER HOWES

1.5miles past Flask Inn turn right into lay - by on right at top of hill. Entrance from lay - by to ruin of old army camp. Padlocked gate and stile there.

Continue on same road for 2miles then turn left to Ravenscar. After 1mile turn left at junction and head north-west to finish at Beacon Howes.

CHECKPOINT SEVEN - BEACON HOWES

Radio mast near Ravenscar and the Lyke Wake Stone.

USEFUL INFORMATION

MILEAGE - OSMOTHERLEY TO RAVENSCAR

Checkpoints	Miles	Times
0 - 1	6	2hours
1 - 2	4	1hour 30mins
2 - 3	10	3hours
3 - 4	5	2hours
4 - 5	8	2hours 20mins
5 - 6	5	1hour 40mins
6 - F	2	30mins
	Total 40	

Based on an approximate walking time of 13hrs, not including breaks at checkpoints. Actual walking times vary depending on the number of walkers and the conditions at time of walk.

Accommodation is limited throughout the route. In Osmotherley there are some B&B's and The Queen Catherine Hotel. In Ravenscar the village hall is available, contact Mrs. Russell on Church Road, Tel. 01723 870801.
Youth Hostels are available (Pre book) in Osmotherley Tel. 01609 883575
Scarborough Tel. 01723 361176

An outdoor shop is in Osmotherley if you forget any equipment or need new items. It is situated in the village centre.

The hills and valleys climbed amount to 5000ft.

The last public telephone after leaving Osmotherley until you arrive at Ravenscar is at Huthwaite Green.

When attempting this challenging walk it is advisable to start around midnight while you are feeling fresh and finish around 4-6pm when you are exhausted but with daylight left. This is even more important during winter months when it gets dark earlier. Leave enough time to finish in daylight allowing extra time at the end for varying weather and walking conditions.

Weather conditions throughout the walk can vary considerably. A calm, still evening in Osmotherley can turn into gale force winds on the tops and torrential rain on route.

In preparing yourself before the walk the best advice is expect rain, cold and wet peat bogs. Anything better is a bonus!

At night, if you are lost but warm and unhurt, find a sheltered area, in heather if possible. Put on warm clothing and keep well covered and out of the wind, use your survival bag. Eat some food before waiting until daylight to establish your position and continue on your way or head for the nearest habitation or telephone. During this period, if at all possible contact your support party. Experience has shown that telephones, CB radios etc., unless very powerful don't work well in this hilly area. Expensive communication equipment will not take kindly to a 42mile rucksack bumping.

You will probably find that having walked 42miles often in cold and wet conditions you may experience problems while getting out of your transport upon arriving home. A hot bath with some bath salts added should help the body to recover quicker.

DISTANCE TO NEAREST MAIN VILLAGES

			Miles	Kms
Start Point	to	Osmotherley	1	1.6
Checkpoint 1	to	Carlton in Cleveland	1.25	2
Checkpoint 2	to	Great Broughton	2.9	4.7
Checkpoint 3	to	Castleton	4	6.4
Checkpoint 4	to	Egton Bridge	5	8
Checkpoint 5	to	Pickering	10.5	16.9
Checkpoint 6	to	Whitby	10	16.1
Beacon Howes	to	Ravenscar	1	1.6

GRID REFERENCES AT MAIN WAY POINTS

Start	470994	
Huthwaite Green	493007	These will be useful for those with a GPS to enable you to find exact positions on route.
Checkpoint 1	523030	
Checkpoint 2	573033	
Bloworth Crossing	616019	
Checkpoint 3	676019	
Road Junction to Bog Section	698012	
Checkpoint 4	744995	
Wheeldale Beck	812983	
Checkpoint 5	857983	
Lilla Howe	889987	
Jugger Howe Ravine	930994	
Checkpoint 6	945004	
Beacon Howes	971012	

HEIGHTS CLIMBED ON ROUTE

	Feet	Metres
Lyke Wake Stone	670	206
Scarth Wood Moor	982	302
Live Moor	1025	315
Carlron Bank	1338	412
Cringle Moor	1427	439
Hasty Bank	1384	425
Botton Head	1490	458
Bloworth Crossing	1274	392
Rosedale Head	1370	421
Loose Howe	1418	436
Shunner Howe	1065	328
Blue Man i 'th'Moss	1043	321
Wheeldale Lodge	550	169
Eller Beck Bridge	564	174
Lilla Howe	959	295
Jugger Howes	630	194
Beacon Howes	871	268

LYKE WAKE DIRGE DICTIONARY

Fleet = Flame;   Neean = none;   beean = bone;   Bon = burn

The Lyke Wake Dirge is a medieval funeral dirge which suggests that everyone after death has to make a journey over difficult moor. If you do various good deeds you will pass various obstacles and get to paradise or Ravenscar whichever you happen to be making for at the time.

Cleveland Lyke Wake Dirge

this yah neet, this yah neet,
ivvery neet an' all,
fire an' fleet an' cannle leet,
an' christ tak up thy saul.

when thoo frae hence away art passed
ivvery neet an' all,
ti whinny moor thoo cums at last,
an' christ tak up thy saul.

if ivver thoo gav owther hosen or shoon,
ivvery neet an' all,
clap thee doon, an' put 'em on,
an' christ tak up thy saul

But if hosen an' shoon thoo nivver gav neean,
ivvery neet an' all,
t' whinnies'll prick thee sair ti t'Beean,
an' christ tak up thy saul.

frae whinny moor when thoo art passed
ivvery neet an' all,
ti t'Brig o' dreead thoo cums at last,
an' christ tak up thy saul.

if ivver thoo gav o' thy siller an' gowd,
ivvery neet an' all,
on t'Brig o' dreead thoo'll finnd foothod
an' christ tak up thy saul.

But if siller an' gowd thoo nivver gavn eean,
ivvery neet an' all,
thoo'll doon, doon tum'le towards hell fleeames,
an' christ tak up thy saul.

frae t'Brig o' dreead when thoo art passed
ivvery neet an' all,
ti t'fleeames o' hell thoo'll cum at last,
an' christ tak up thy saul

if ivver thoo gav owther Bite or sup,
ivvery neet an' all,
t' fleeames'll nivver catch thee up,
an' christ tak up thy saul.

But if Bite or sup thoo nivver gav neean,
ivvery neet an' all,
t' flames'll Bon thee sair ti t'Beean,
an' christ tak up thy saul

27

MINDLESS
VIOLENCE

ALEX HILL

WILD VAULT
PUBLISHING

THIS IS SOHO — LOCAL NEWS AND VIEWS
Murdered, and mutilated girl found hanging in Soho Street.

By Mary Kelly

A teenage girl who was brutally murdered and mutilated, had both her breasts cut off and her body burned, police say.

Details of the gruesome murder surfaced after the body was discovered by a passer-by on Berwick Street, at around 8 AM on May 20.

The victim has so far remained unidentified, but police believe she may have been a teenage prostitute. If this were confirmed, that would represent the third killing of its kind in the last four weeks.

Police have been quick to quash speculation that these murders are connected and have given little credibility to rumours circulating Soho about a killer who is targeting young working girls.

Police spokesperson Commander Steve Knight told This is Soho: 'We're well aware of the gossip going around at the moment, but I can categorically state that these murders are random and isolated incidents. There is no serial killer.'

Well, there you have it, readers! I don't know about you, but I'm not convinced.

It is the opinion of this part—time journalist that Steve Knight is talking out of his arse.

If you're reading this, you girls be careful out there.

Jack

Ye poor wee lassie! What has he done tae ye? The sick bastard. I'll get him for this, see if ah don't.

Ye havnae been dead long – yer body stuffed inside a sleepin bag n tossed intae the garbage like a used tissue. The dried semen oan yer skin tells me everythin ah need tae know, but the bastard hadnae stopped there. He's slashed open yer face from ear tae ear n hacked out yer tongue.

Ah dig the Rothmans packet from mah raincoat n stick one between mah lips.

– You can't smoke here, a scene ay crime officer says tae me, sae ah slip past the police cordon. Oan the other side ay the street, two uniforms are bein loaded intae ambulances oan stretchers. One ay them is proper fucked – his face is a bloody mask – looks like someone has tried tae beat him tae death.

What the hell happened here? Place is a circus choreographed tae the wail ay sirens.

Ah light up the fag n take a burst ay nicotine. Damn that feels good. The pleasure doesnae last long – quickly replaced by a cripplin pain in mah side.

Ah know ah should quit. The doctor told me as much, but what was the point? The horse has nae just bolted from the barn, but he's changed his identity n flown tae fuckin Mexico.

Aam already a dead man walkin, sae why deny mahself the only thing that gives me any kind ay joy, albeit a masochistic n surprisingly painful kind ay joy.

The consultant used his fist tae demonstrate the size ay the tumour chewin through mah lung. He would later tell me the cancer had spread tae mah liver n stomach, sae ah was fucked. Words like 'inoperable' n 'palliative care' were also used, which meant ah was doubly fucked.

Truth is, eh'd suspected somethin was wrong long before that rainy afternoon. There had been the chronic fatigue, the chest pains, the weight loss – all ay which had been self-explained away. Ah must be drinkin tae much, workin tae hard or nae gettin enough sleep – that's why ah cannae move mah legs in the mornin.

Head. Sand. Buried.

Thing is, it's easy tae lie tae yerself, but it's nae sae easy tae lie tae other people, especially when those people are paid tae stick their noses in other people's shit.

Every detective at the Nick thinks they're fuckin Poirot! They would make moronic statements, like 'ooh, you've lost weight', sae ah invented 'The Diet'.

That kept them happy for a while, but the compliments soon dried up when mah cheekbones started pokin through skin. That prompted calls for me tae quit 'The Diet', but the lies continued. Ah took up marathon runnin despite a lifelong aversion tae sweat. Ah suffered bouts ay food poisonin, unfairly blamed oan The Star ay India – our local curry house. Many colleagues had boycotted the restaurant cos ay mah lies. Sorry about that, Raj.

What choice did ah have? Tell them the truth? Ah can live with all the pain in the world, but ah don't want any cunt givin me sympathy. Ah don't want those pityin looks. Ye know the kind aam talkin about. The look you'd give a kitten locked out in the rain.

Ah toss the fag butt intae the drain.

– You should do that with the whole packet. I thought I told you to quit.

Ah turn n smile at DI Nikki Cooper. - Ah will soon, Doc, ah promise.

Mah mind flashes back tae the last time ah saw her - back in the hospital after eh'd collapsed in Brannin's office. How humilatin.

- I'm surprised to see you here, she says tae me. - I thought you were going to take some time.

- Ah thought ah might know the victim.

- And did you?

- Nae.

- But you were expecting someone?

- Aye.

- Who?

- It doesnae matter. You'll just think aam nuts.

- I thought you vice boys knew all the girls who worked Soho.

- Nae this one, but ah can tell ye one thing: she's not your average teen hooker. Ah dinnae see any tracks oan her arms, sae ah reckon you're lookin at a high-class underager caterin for the more discernin paedo.

- Do you know any pimps or agencies who'd supply girls like that?

- Aye, ah know a few, ah say, exhalin smoke from mah nostrils. - Ah don't suppose any ay this looks familiar tae ye?

Nikki rolls her eyes. - Don't start this again!

- Start what?

- You know!

- You're tellin me none ay this looks familiar?

- I know what you're gonna say but.....

- That's four now, Nikki.

- You know what'll happen if Branning hears you spouting this stuff again? He's on his way down here.

- Aam nae scared ay that bastard.

– Well, I am! It's my arse that gets chewed every time he catches me talking to you.

– An what a nice arse it is! ah say without thinkin.

Now Nikki looks embarrassed. Mah cheeks are burnin up, sae ah change the subject, before an uncomfortable silence gobbles us up n shits us out.

– What's with the sideshow? ah ask, pointin tae the uniforms bein loaded intae the ambulance.

– I don't know – some weirdo turned up and started messing with the body. When uniform tried to restrain him, he did that to them.

– Jesus Christ, ah hope he's in a cell gettin a good fuckin kickin!

– No, he got away, but we got a description. We'll find him. Oh shit!

Nikki's got a, 'a've shat mahself' face oan her n now ah see why – Detective Chief Inspector Dean Brannin charges toward us wi the grace ay an elephant wearin Doc Marten's.

– What the fuck are you doing here?

– Ah was just passin.

– Well, you can pass off!

– Maybe ah can help.

– Listen to me, you knock-kneed Scotch wanker – we don't need assistance from a nut job. This is a murder case – that means for the big boys only. You're a vice cop, so why don't you fuck off and do what vice cops do? I hear they've got a special on in Chinatown – two wanks for the price of one! Go on, knock yourself out.

Ah wish ah could say somethin back – some kind ay witty retort but mah mind has gone on a business trip tae The Bahamas. I'll probably think ay somethin tae say in twenty minutes when it's tae late. If he wasnae such a big fucker, eh'd smack him in the gob, but ah keep quiet n take it.

Nikki gives me a, 'ah told ye sae' shrug as she follows Brannin back tae the crime scene.

– Fuckin idiot, ah whisper under mah breath.

A cold wind hits me n ah see somethin move in the corner ay mah eye – somethin up oan the roof ay Dirty Ken's bookstore. Is that a person up there? Nae possible, unless they're made ay shadow.

Yer losin it, ye old bastard. Maybe the cancer's spread tae mah brain, makin me see things that arenae there, or maybe it's the Grim Reaper, eyein me up like Ronald McDonald at a cow show.

Let him try it – ah willnae go quietly, I'll tell ye that much!

Maybe he's come for ye, mah poor wee lassie. Ah look back at ye stretched out oan the cold pavement with only a sheet tae cover yer modesty – thinkin about that sadistic grin carved intae yer face.

Were ye laughin? Maybe ye were laughin at me – everyone else does, why should ye be any different?

After all, yer pain is over. Mine is just beginnin.

Laura

Manic Monday.

The Bangles are playing on repeat in my head this morning. I should thank Mum and Dad for that – they're the ones who raised me on a diet of eighties cheese – something I look back on and realise was nothing more than a subtle and socially acceptable form of child abuse.

For years, I pleaded with them, to expand their minds, to listen to something not composed during a dark age when shoulder pads were considered cool and permed mullets were obligatory for male sex symbols.

I remember one time they'd buckled and agreed to play my Girls Aloud CD in the living room, the social hub of Whistleford Cottage. The looks on their faces still haunt me – Dad wailed like he was being indecently assaulted, and Mum covered her ears like they might leap off her head.

Looking back, they may have had a point, but they didn't give it a chance – they just switched it off and played Alphaville's Big in Japan.

I find it hard to believe that Alphaville have been big anywhere at any time.

What I wouldn't give for this train to crash. Just a small collision or a little shunt – something to shake me up and give me an excuse not to go into work. I wouldn't want anyone to get hurt or anything like that.

I should have called in sick – that's what people normally do, isn't it? I could be tucked up in bed if I'd planned this correctly.

The train pulls into Blackheath station, and commuters swarm onto the already packed carriage. Moans and groans follow as the squeeze hits.

Somebody shouts.

– Can you move down a bit, please?

– There's no room! Comes the angry response.

At least I managed to get a seat, unlike the poor souls crushed into the aisle. I can relate – the chubby lady, who squished herself next to me and is acquainting me with the window, has halved my own seat.

It's okay, lady, I didn't feel like breathing today.

As if reading my thoughts, she wiggles her bottom, encroaching further into my space. I give her an evil look, and now she stares at me like I'm something that needs to be scraped from her shoe.

Excuse me for existing. I should say something but decide against it for fear of causing a scene. I don't want to come across as fattist. In this day and age, appearing to be anything-*ist* can get you into serious trouble.

They could at least turn the heating down. Don't they realise it's twenty-two degrees outside? South East Rail extort literally millions of pounds from customers every year, offering a sub-standard service of train delays – you'd think they could fork out for some air con.

I take out my phone and check the time: 7:45 AM.

Only forty-five minutes until I'm at work, and my worst fear is realised. Maybe the train will come hurtling off the tracks. Don't say things like that, Laura, you silly girl! That's what anxiety does – it makes you stupid, killing rational thought, spinning you off in a million different directions so you can't focus on things that matter.

Looking around the carriage, I notice I'm not the only one feeling like this. Everyone's got this slapped-arse face thing going on, looking like they'd rather be anywhere else.

Surely life shouldn't be like this – packed into trains and offices, forced to spend our lives surrounded by strangers, filling endless minutes talking bullshit, trying to look intellectual when really, we're just as clueless as everybody else.

What happened to my dreams? I was going to be a ballet dancer or an actress or a writer. The world had been filled with so many possibilities, and now Father Time was slamming the door on all of them.

What happened to that sweet little girl who had the world at her feet?

She's long gone. Dead and buried.

Get a job, get a career, and move to London – that's what Mum drummed into me. Great fucking advice, Mum! Are you happy now? You've turned your only daughter into a cast member from The Walking Dead.

Come to think of it – even mindless zombies wouldn't be seen dead working nine to five. And now Dolly Parton croons in my head, but it isn't nine to five anymore, is it, Dolly? More like eight–thirty to six–thirty, but I doubt that would've sold many records.

Maybe work won't be as bad as I'm making out. Nice try, but it's going to be terrible. You've got to deliver that presentation today – remember? You've got to stand up in front of all those people and talk about the positive impact of the company's new recruitment system. That'll be fun for the audience. Maybe I should be merciful and distribute cyanide capsules and razor blades.

Have I thought of anything to say yet? And what if I say the wrong thing? What if I freeze up and don't say anything at all? Remember that presentation at school – didn't go very well did it?

My heart races. Sweat seeps into my shirt. Why won't someone put on some air conditioning? I open up the newspaper, scanning the headlines, hoping it'll take my mind from the fear.

The first five pages confront me with rape, murder, and grim economic predictions about my financial future.

I read about Lisa Traynor, the young single mother whose baby boy was snatched from his pushchair in broad daylight. Lisa looks terrible in her photograph, as you'd expect. Her face is bloated with tears – eyes red and sore. Now I feel a little better about my problems. The cynic in me wonders if that's why they hand out these free morning papers – to remind you there's always some poor sod worse off than yourself.

I do a lot of flipping before I come across anything remotely positive – an interview with Hollywood actress Jennifer Clucas, talking about how a stranger turned her life around with a random act of kindness. I don't know whether I'm happy for her or resentful – probably tucked somewhere neatly between the two. Life is very much a game of chance – right place, wrong time – should I turn left or right? It's scary how a single decision can influence so much.

What if I pull the alarm and bring this train to a shuddering halt? What's the worst that could happen? But it's too late – the train is pulling into London Bridge.

Now I'm on the platform, swept along by the commuters shepherding me toward the ticket barriers and the unforgiving city waiting beyond.

Cattle knowingly walking toward the slaughterhouse.

And to think it's only Monday morning – still five full working days until the weekend. But then something occurs to me – something that makes me forget about the presentation and the office waiting to chew me up.

I think about how I'd spent ten minutes with my head down the toilet this morning. I think about those eight letters written in blue.

I stroke my belly and bite my lip – I'm not looking forward to telling Josh that I'm pregnant.

Linton

Sum men are lucky an sum ain't.

One man wins the lottery an anotha gets shot in the same nite. Who wud think I'd be standin on this balcony, lookin out on them green fields with a glass ah Hennessy in my hand, so far from that shithole where I grew up? I couldn't be furtha away in my country mansion, smokin a cuban cigar, feelin like Scarface.

– Daddy?

I turn round an see my dawta, Madeline behind me. She's wearin them Dora the Explora pyjamas I bought er for Christmas, lookin like an angel wiv that innocent face an them green eyes.

How did a bad man like me produce somethin so beautiful an pure?

– What's wrong my little princess? You shud be in bed.

– I can't sleep, she says. – The music is too loud.

– Okay, my darlin, let's see if we can get yuh uncle Carl tuh turn it down.

I stub out my cigar an lead er into the house. Tunes are goin off in the livin room. People are fuckin on my carpet.

Odessa stares at me from the sofa – she looks bashy tonite wiv er caramel skin an that tight mini–skirt she's wearin. I'm alreddi two steps toward er wen I rememba I'm still oldin Madeline's and, suh I call Charlotte from the kitchen.

– Put Madeline tuh bed, I say tuh er. – She can't sleep an wants er mum tuh tuck er in.

– Why can't you do it?

There ain't nothin more unattractive than a woman who talks back, suh I give er a look like I'm gonna knock er teeth out. - Cos I'm gonna be fuckin that bitch ova there! Now do as I say, before I throw you out on the street!

Er eyes follow my finga pointed at Odessa an now it looks like she's gonna bawl.

I yell at er an show er the back a' my and. - What a' yuh still doing ere, woman?

She scurries from the room like sum diseased rat, draggin Madeline wiv her.

What tha fuck does she expect? Treatin me like a bad man. I ad offered tuh pay for plastic surgery. I wud pay tuh get that arse lifted an to firm up them tits, but she ad refused.

Ungrateful bitch!

Odessa comes ova an presses herself against me. - I thought she would never leave, she says.

That's when I ear Cassius behind me. - Excuse me, Boss! he says.

Cassius is wider than most men are tall. He's proper hench too - looks like he's got bricks under that skin. First time I saw him was at a bare-knuckle fight. No man wud fight him, suh they put a Rottweiler in wiv im.

He eld that poor ting down, stranglin it as tears ran down his face. Straight after, I ired im as my bodyguard - surely no one wud fuck wiv me when he was at my side. Most motherfuckers crossed the street just tuh avoid im.

- I'm awful sorry to disturb you, Boss, he says. - Seth is here and wants to see you.

- Can't yuh see I'm busy? Wat makes you fink I wanna talk tuh that pussy'ole?

- He's real insistent, says it's important.

- What can be more important than this? I say, grabbin Odessa's arse.

– He wouldn't give me any details, but he said it's about Yuri.

– Fuck! You sure he said, Yuri?

– Yeah, I fink so.

That sneaky Russian's name sends blood from my dick tuh clenched fists.

– Where's Seth now?

– Waitin in your office.

I turn tuh Odessa. – I'm sorry babe, but we got tuh postpone, I've got some business I need to attend tuh.

She pushes erself back on me. – Screw that babe, don't you wanna fuck? You sum kinda queer or sumthin?

Wivout a word, I thump her in the face. There ain't no one alive who can call Linton Johnson a battyman!

I find Seth in the study, runnin his finga ova my books.

– I didn't take you for a Dickens fan, he says, pointin tuh Great Expectations.

– What tha fuck are you sayin? Yuh callin me illiterate or sumfin?

And now suddenly he's backtrackin – mumblin like a retard wiv all them, I'm so sorries an I didn't mean any offences. I luv torturin this pussy'ole – course I neva read no Dickens, but I ain't havin this little bitch lookin down on me.

I'm pretty sure I'm gonna kill this fool wen he's nuh longa useful. See, I don't like Babylon, an I certainly don't like corrupt Babylon who use their position tuh extort money from me.

– What yuh doin here, anyway? I ask im. – Can't yuh see I'm entertainin?

– Yes, sorry, but this couldn't wait. I have some information you'll want to hear.

– What kinda information?

– I've heard someone's looking to make a move on you – and soon!

– Where did yuh hear this?

– Unfortunately, I'm not at liberty to say right now.

Fuckin ell, all this lawyerly chat is makin my ead urt.

– Listen, yuh little fassy'ole, I pay yuh tuh look after my interests. If I ask a question, I expect yuh tuh ansah it.

– I can't tell you my source, but I promise you this information is one hundred percent reliable.

– Suh who's the fool wiv a death wish?

– I can't tell you that either.

– Okay, I'm gettin annoyed now. Are yuh tryin tuh make me mad?

– I assure you, all your questions will be answered soon.

Now he's playin wiv his mobile. It buzzes in his hand.

– Sorry, am I keepin yuh from sumfin important? Yuh told Cassius yuh had sum information about Yuri?

Seth looks up from his mobile. He's got a strange look on his face. – Yes, he says. – I have some information about Yuri. You don't need to worry about him muscling in on your patch anymore. In fact, you don't need to worry about anything ever again!

There's a loud crash downstairs, followed by screams – the kinda screams yuh hear wen a bitch gets a tool pushed in er face.

– What the fuck? I say, openin up my desk drawa weh I keep my Glock.

Empty.

– Missing something, Linton?

I look up an see Seth's got my own gun pointed at me. – Are you mad?

He starts laughin an now I'm tryin tuh work out ow this prick has turned the tables on me.

The shouts an noise continue downstairs – I hear a strange grindin sound. The whole house shakes. An suddenly, I'm finkin about my little girl. I need to get outta this room an make sure Madeline's safe.

I step toward Seth.

– Don't move, he says, aimin the gun at my leg. – I'm under strict instructions not to kill you, but I've got no problem maiming you!

– Strict instructions from who? Yuh betta tell me who put yuh up to this shit.

– Be careful what you wish for!

– I'm gonna give yuh two seconds tuh put that gun down or I swear I'm gonna beat yuh tuh death wiv it. I take another step an then find myself on the floor, gunshot ringin in my ears.

I look down at the hole in my leg, leakin blood. – Yuh stupid muthafucker! Yuh know who you're fuckin wiv?

Seth says nothin – he picks out a 5 iron from my golf clubs an stands ova me.

– Four! he says.

Then he swings.

Joe

Alcoholics don't worry about usual trivialities like paying the mortgage, earning good money, or not upsetting people. Your primary concern is knowing when and where your next drink is coming from.

Most normal people faced with my current predicament would probably ask: *how did you end up on the top deck of this bus* or *why are you wearing this dress*, but all I can do is salivate over the prospect of murdering a bottle of T'Bird fortified wine.

I check my reflection in the window, and I'm horrified to see my face is made up – thick mascara on eyelashes, rouge on the cheeks, and dark crimson lipstick. Last thing I remember was buying drinks for two twenty-something-year old girls in The Wheatsheaf – at least I think they were girls.

To be fair, I'd been pretty wasted.

Need to think back.

Brain – please access memory files from the last twelve hours.

Brain replies: Are you sure you wanna do that? I'm receiving a warning that the requested files may contain embarrassing and emotionally crippling material.

Yes, Brain, I'm sure. I need to know.

Request denied. Files are inaccessible. Fuck! Maybe it took a peek and decided not to share in an act of self-preservation – the brain can't survive if the body dies of shame.

I look out the window and see a run-down high street I don't recognise.

Where am I, and how do I get home? And where is my wallet?

Quick, check your pockets!

What pockets? You're wearing a dress!

I search the seats around me.

No joy – Fuck! And what about my ring? Do I still have it?

I check my left hand and breathe a sigh of relief.

Still there. The diamond solitaire glints on my little finger.

Where is this bus going? Maybe to Hell. I see a sign for Lewisham, and suddenly Hell doesn't sound so bad.

Chances are, it'll turn around and take me back to Central London, but that could take ages, and I desperately need a drink. The shakes will hit soon, and no one wants to see that.

But that's not what's worrying me. The Hunger will be in my ear again soon. Alcohol is the only thing that silences it.

The bus stops. I hear drunken female voices accompanied by the clatter of high heels on the stairs. Two sixteen or seventeen-year-old girls materialise from the stairwell. They're pretty enough, despite their multi-coloured hairdos and metal shit in their faces.

They sit at the front, rabbiting on about some pop gig they've just been to.

– Oh, he's so fit, isn't he? one of them says.

– Yeah, he's soooo fit and don't even get me started on his voice.

They carry on like this for what seems like hours, and I'm on the verge of tears by the time we arrive at the next stop, where five snotty looking punks announce their arrival on the top deck by being as loud and obnoxious as possible.

I duck down and hide – I really don't want them to see me dressed like this. Thankfully, they don't even glance at me – they zero in on the girls like a pride of lions stalking prey.

– You alright, darlin? one punk says, leaning over, forcing them to sit uncomfortably forward.

– Yes, I'm okay, thank you, one girl replies – she couldn't be colder if she were in Antarctica.

– My name's Keith! You see my pal over there, he really fancies you and wants your phone number.

– Sorry, but I have a boyfriend.

– Ah, fuck him! He's probably a bum basher anyway. Giv'us ya number then.

– Okay, she says. – It's one two three four five six seven.....

– You're not funny, you know!

– Sorry, I don't mean to be rude, but we were in the middle of a conversation.

– Yeah, I know, and now you're in a conversation with us.

– It's a private conversation!

– Are you saying you want us to leave?

– Yes, please.

– Why are you bein so rude? You gotta real chip on your shoulder.

– Then you'll want to leave us alone, won't you?

I keep myself low and cover my ears. Why won't these arseholes shut up? I've got a shitty hangover and can't handle this right now. I need to find some booze before The Hunger finds me.

– *But I've already found you*, it says. The maniac glee in the voice terrifies me. – *What are you so afraid of? Am I really that bad? After all, you need me. You say you don't, but you always come running back sooner or later, don't you?*

Fuck off! You're not even real. You're just a voice in my head.

– *I'm so much more than that. I'm a part of you. You can deny it as much as you like, but I'll always be here – waiting until you need me again.*

I'll never need you – not ever!

– *We'll see. Listen! Their voices are getting louder. Can you smell the anger, the rage – the fear?*

The strained conversation between the girls and the chimpanzees has escalated into a slagging match.

– Please will you leave us alone!

– Not until you giv us ya number.

– I'm not giving you anything.

– Fuckin lesbian!

– I'm a lesbian because I'm not into bestiality.

Keith doesn't like that one bit. He leans forward and grabs her hair, raising a closed fist.

– Leave her alone! a voice calls out – a strangely familiar voice.

Everyone looks back at me with mouths hung in a silent 'what did the cat just drag in?'

Now I realise the voice must've belonged to me.

A smile appears on Keith's face. – Jesus Christ, what the fuck have you come as? You know Halloween isn't until October!

– I said, 'leave her alone'.

– Fuck off mate, shouldn't you be busy suckin off blokes down the Blue Oyster bar?

The boys laugh – their pig-like faces flushed red.

And now The Hunger is in my ear – so loud now.

– *Look what you've become. You're just a freak in a dress. I bet they wouldn't laugh at me. Why don't you let me out to play? Just for a short time. I promise I'll be good. Go on, you know you want to.*

– Fuck off, you cunt!!!

Oh fuck! I must have shouted that out loud because Keith is on his feet, charging toward me.

– What did you call me, weirdo?

– I wasn't talking to you. I was talking to...

– Who?

– Nobody.

– Oh deeeeaaaaaar! You really are fucked up, aren't you?

– *Jesus, this brain–dead Neanderthal has certainly got you banged to rights. You do need help – you're a tragic waste of skin.*

I try and force the voice from my head, but it won't leave. My stomach burns. I'm so hungry now. I cover my ears.

Please leave me alone.

– *I'll never leave you. You need me. You're going to let me out, aren't you? You know you are. Just get it over with and stop being a little cock tease.*

Now Keith is sat next to me, leaning so close I can see the glint of his gold earring and the bacteria slithering on his skin.

He hits me on the side of the head – not hard, but hard enough to piss me off.

– Stop doing that, I say.

– Or what? What the fuck are you going to do, weirdo?

– *Yes, what are you going to do? I bet you're not going to do anything, but I can. I can make everything better. I can make that hunger in your gut go away, and I can make this greasy wank stain, and his slippery malformed half–brothers fuck off too.*

But there are five of them.

– *So what? We've faced worse odds, or don't you remember? Besides when the other four see what I do to this spotty bastard, they'll shit their pants. They always do!*

I don't know... they're pretty drunk. Alcohol can make people do silly things – just look how I'm dressed.

– I tell you what, why don't we make a little wager? I'll bet a tenner they'll want nothing to do with us once I redecorate this bus with this cunting fuck!

You're on!

Danny hits me again, harder this time. My stomach gurgles...consuming itself.

Something clicks in my head. A key turns.

Time must've passed – someone pressed the fast forward button on my life. Things haven't worked out so well for Keith in the next frame. He writhes on the floor, clutching his forearm, which wobbles like jelly – looks like every bone has been smashed to bits, and only skin holds everything together. The side of his face is covered with blood. He screams like a stuck pig.

I look down at my closed hand, almost afraid to look. I open it up and see the gold earring nestled neatly in the palm – a chunk of bloody earlobe still attached.

Keith's companions are on their feet, but they're backing away. Now they see what I am for the first time, and they do not like what they see.

Macho bullshit leaks from arseholes.

– Told you these little maggots would bottle it, The Hunger says. *– That's a tenner you owe me.*

You were right – too bad I've lost my wallet, isn't it?

I study the faces of everyone on the top deck. They all look scared – even the girls.

I want to see what they see, so I check my reflection in the window.

A shudder runs down my spine when I see the smile on my face.

Linton

– Wakey wakey, rise and shine, Sleeping Beauty, Seth says, pourin water on my ead.

I'm tied tuh a chair in my livin room – my bruvva Carl is tied beside me – his face is badly beaten.

My party guests are hogtied an lined up across the carpet. Charlotte stares at me fru teary eyes. Blood pumps fru me as I wrestle against my restraints, but they don't budge.

Carl gives me a look tuh say, 'yuh fink I dinnt try that alreddi'.

A man dressed in tactical gear steps forward – he's oldin a pump-action shotgun – yuh know that crazy gun Arnie has in Terminator 2. He's wearin a Justin Bieber latex mask, which covers his ole ead.

– You can struggle all you want, Justin says. – But you should know, I used to be a Cub Scout, and tying knots is my speciality.

There are two other men wiv Justin – both dressed in black an wearin masks. I recognise Harry Styles from the poster on Madeline's bedroom wall, but I don't know who the other guy is sposed to be.

Oh, my God, Madeline – where is my sweet dawta? Keep quiet – maybe she's hidin an they ain't found er yet.

An where is Cassius? I can't see im either. Maybe he laid low wen they burst in. Maybe he's called the cavalry. I just need tuh bide my time until he makes his move – need tuh keep these fools chattin. They must want sumfin from me or I'd be dead alreddi.

– What do yuh want?

Another voice answas from the back ah the room.

– I want to see you how you are now – squirmin an shittin your pants, desperately tryin to think of a way out of the fuck-ole predicament you've found yourself in!

Seth must've hit me really ard on the ead – I can barely see the figure standin in the shadows.

He steps into the light, showin the Donald Trump mask ova his ead. What is that lyin at his feet?

Nuh nuh it ain't possible.

Blood covers ninety percent ah the body. White bones poke out from what remains ah Cassius. I ain't eva seen a body look like this. What did they do tuh him?

Trump steps forward. Blood drips from the blade of the chainsaw in his ands. He removes his mask, revealin the scariest face I've ever seen – Hannibal Lecter's worst nightmare. He's got a scary grin – a grin I recognise.

It can't be...it can't be..please...nuh.

– What's the matter, Linton? Dunnt ya recognise me?

But I do recognise im.

His name is on my tongue, but I can't bring myself tuh say it.

A warm sensation spreads thru the lowa half ah my body as I whispa one word – a name.

– Clay!

Now they all laugh at me.

Then I realise that I've gone an pissed myself.

Joe

Boris stares at me in the rearview mirror.

I can't work out what bothers him most – that he's got a six-foot two transvestite riding in the back of his Mercedes or that I haven't showered for thirty-six hours.

Probably both.

I look down at my hands – fingers tremble. Withdrawal is biting hard, and I'm pretty sure I'm about to chuck.

– Do you have anything to drink? I ask Boris.

He shoots another look in the rearview mirror.

– I don't think your brother would like that! he says.

He's not my brother, I want to snap, but I bite my tongue rather than the hand driving me home. – Look at me! You can see I'm sick – I need it!

– Okay, keep your knickers on, sweetheart. He opens up the glove compartment and pulls out a bottle of Teachers. – Now you didn't get this from me, right?

– Yeah yeah, I say, snatching the bottle, unscrewing the lid before you can say 'paint stripper'. Usually, I give Teachers a wide berth, but right now, I'd drink cat's piss if it'd lift me out of this slump.

Now The Hunger is back and whispering in my ear.

– *You're a real classy guy!*

Not you again. I thought I got rid of you.

– *I'm not going anywhere.*

I take five long gulps, hoping the warm liquid will wash the voice from my mind.

– Seriously, you can't tell Charlie you got that bottle from me, Boris says. – I don't want him thinking I'm drinking on the job.

– Your secret's safe with me.

I couldn't give a fuck if Boris snowballed heroin while driving Charlie around. I wouldn't care if he drove them both into the Thames. Secretly, I'd prayed for it many times. Life would be much simpler if they both fucked off and died.

I look out the Merc window and see we're already in Soho, passing titty bars and sex shops. We turn onto Shaftesbury Avenue and park up outside Tierney's bar, which doubles as Charlie's office.

Boris clicks off the ignition and turns back to me. – So, are you cummin in voluntarily, or do I have to drag you in?

– You're welcome to try, you big bald fuck!

That upsets him. Boris has always been sensitive about his hairline, or lack of it. Once, he'd experimented with wearing a toupee, which looked like he was balancing a dead rat on his head.

– Don't make this any harder than it needs to be. Remember you'd still be in the Nick if it wasn't for your brother.

There it is – that word again – brother. If Boris uses it once more, I'm going to force-feed him this Teachers – glass bottle n'all. Charlie has been a great many things to me, but never a brother – either by blood or by action. Our association was a marriage of circumstance, a cruel twist of fate that had left us both damaged in so many ways.

– Okay, let's get this over with, I say, opening the car door and stepping out.

The bar is mostly empty, which doesn't surprise me. Most normal people – the ones with more than half a brain cell, avoid this place like the plague. Two American tourists came in once to ask for directions and barely left with their underwear.

Scruples, the barman – aptly named because he doesn't have any – double-takes when he clocks my dress, shakes his head, then continues filling glasses from the drip tray.

A group of Charlie's goons play cards and drink vodka at a round table in the far corner. I feel their eyes all over me.

One of them smiles, showing off crooked teeth.

– Nice dress, he says in a thick Russian accent.

I give him an evil look, and now he studies his cards intently. I'm not surprised – no one wants to get a kicking from a transvestite in front of their mates.

Boris knocks on the door at the back of the bar.

– Come! A familiar voice calls from inside.

The door opens to reveal Charlie reclining in a swivel seat behind his desk.

He greets me with a raised eyebrow. – Jesus Christ!

– Not quite, I say.

– Look at the state of you. Do you know what you look like?

– Yeah, I get it – I look like an idiot.

– I wouldn't say that. I think we may have found your look.

– Get fucked!

– Did that last night, already.

– I thought you were sitting funny, I say. – I hope he told you he loved you.

– At least I'm not wearing a fuckin dress!

– Is that why you brought me back here? To take the piss out of me because if you did, I'm gonna need another drink. This bottle of piss your driver gave me is giving me double vision. I turn to Boris and grin at him. – Oh shit! I wasn't supposed to tell Charlie about your drinking problem, was I, Boris?

Boris's eyes widen and he stutters.

– It's okay, Boris, you can leave now, Charlie says, gesturing to the door.

 – Yeah, fuck off, Boris! I say.

Boris leaves, but not before fixing me a death stare.

– Why you got to be so hard on Boris? Charlie asks me.

– Because I can't stand that bald cunt. The light hurts my eyes when it reflects off his head.

– You haven't been taking the piss out of his hair, have you?

– What hair?

– He may not look it, but he's sensitive. He really takes it to heart.

– I don't give a fuck if Boris chucks himself off the nearest bridge. I'll be happy to give him a push if he needs it.

– You've got a lot of repressed anger, haven't you, Joe?

– You're one to talk! Anyway, that fucker is a fucking rat.

– Boris ain't no rat.

– Trust me, Charlie, you'll save yourself prison time if you kill that fucker.

I move over to the walnut drinks cabinet, grab myself a glass, and pour the most expensive-looking liquid I can find.

– Do you know what that is?

– No, but it's wet so I'll drink it.

– It's a rare Dalmore - six hundred quid a bottle.

– I'll try not to spill any.

I take a swig. Fuck me – it tastes so good. I think it may actually be fucking my mouth. I've never had a throat orgasm before, but I wouldn't rule it out right now.

– So, what do you think?

– It's alright. I've had better.

– You could at least pour me one.

– You've got arms, haven't you?

– I thought you'd be more grateful – after all, you'd still be festering in a police cell if it wasn't for me. And let me tell you, it wasn't easy – I had to call in a few favours to get you out.

– I never asked for your help. The first I knew about it was when Kojak rocked up at the police station. I could've happily gone the rest of my life without seeing your self-satisfied face again.

– Is this any way to talk to your brother?

My fist tightens around the crystal tumbler. Glass creaks. Knuckles whiten.

– You're not my brother!

– How can you say these things to me? Haven't I always done right by you?

– No.

– That's like a knife through my heart. I've never wanted anything but the best for you. And I gotta say, I'm really worried about you. I mean, look at you. I knew you hit the bottle, but just how fucked up do you have to get to wind up dressed like Dame Edna Everidge's worst nightmare? On top of that, you've now taken to ripping schoolboys' ears off.

– He was not a schoolboy!

– Look, I'm not judging. I'm excited that you can still hurt people, but school kids – there's a line, and you're a long way over it. If you want to bust heads, you know there's a job for you here. We could have the old dream team back together again.

– Thanks for the offer, but I think I'd rather have something large and pointy rammed up my arse.

– I think you've spent too much time in Soho.

– I'm retired, Charlie.

– That's not what I hear.

– What's that supposed to mean?

– I may lock myself away in this office, but I still hear things, you know.

– Oh yeah?

– Yeah, like I heard one of Nikolai Novichkov's clubs got rolled over last week.

– Really, I'm shocked.

– Yeah apparently some guy walked into the club, wearing a balaclava and single-handedly beat the living shit out of five blokes with his bare hands. Can you believe that – with his bare fucking hands?

– Sounds like a tragedy.

– You're telling me. Made off with over two hundred grand too.

– Doesn't sound like a bad day's work.

– But will he live to spend it? Word is, Novichkov has been tearing London apart looking for this guy, but I don't suppose you know anything about this.

– No, I don't.

– Of course not, but sooner or later Novichkov is gonna ask me if I know anything. I'd be far more likely to stick my neck out for someone who's working with me.

– I'm not coming back, Charlie.

– If you say so. I'm just trying to give you a helping hand. After all, I promised Charlotte I'd look out for you when she was gone.

– Don't you dare! Don't you dare say her name!

– Why not? She was my sister, my blood after all.

– Only in name. She wanted nothing to do with you because she knew what you were.

– And what am I?

– A cancerous leech preying on the misery of others. And when exactly did you and Charlotte have this imaginary conversation? When she was in the hospital? Funny, because I don't remember you being there!

– I'm just happy she never got to see you like this. What would she think if she could see you now?

– She can't think anything, Charlie – she's dead. She's rotting in the ground, and there's not a thing either of us can do about it.

I finish off my tumbler, lay the empty glass on the desk, and head out of the door, but not before I've swiped the bottle of Dalmore.

Outside, the sunshine hurts my eyes.

A young blonde – one of Charlie's girls leans up against next door's shop window, smoking a cigarette. She's heavily made up, but that doesn't disguise she's blatantly underage. I'd guess fifteen tops but could be younger.

I gesture to her cigarette. – Can I ponce one of those?

She gives me a surly look – the kind of look only a fifteen-year old girl can give.

– These cost money, you know!

– That's what I hear.

She rolls her eyes and offers me the open packet.

I take three.

– Are you taking the piss?

– I'll pay you back next time, I say. – I'm gonna need a light.

She passes me a Zippo.

– That's a nice dress by the way, she says. – The colour really matches your eyes.

– I'm so glad you think so.

– Heavy night was it?

– No, I like dressing like this. Do you work for Charlie?

– Is it that obvious?

– I'm afraid so.

– Well, it could be worse. I only have to work for the scumbag, but I could be his brother or something really embarrassing like that.

– I'm not his brother.

– That's not what everyone else says.

– Well 'everyone else' is full of shit!

– That's one of life's eternal truths.

– Aren't you a little young to be spouting philosophy?

– Aren't you a little too male to be wearing mascara?

– Touché.

We share a long silence, enjoying the sweet taste of nicotine. It looks as though she's about to say something intelligent and thought provoking. I should have known better.

– Who's Les? she asks. – Do you think that's the name of the main character?

She's pointing at something across the street.

I look at the Shaftesbury Theatre, up into the face of the haunted girl looking down on us. – You are joking, right? It's French. Les Miserables means 'The Miserable' in French.

Now she's looking at me as though I'm an ageing dinosaur with no more right to live on God's green earth than a genital ulcer.

– How am I supposed to know that? Do I look like a literary scholar?

– No, you do not, I say.

– So, what has she got to be so miserable about?

– She's alive, isn't she?

– Aren't you fun to be around?

– I have my moments.

– Well, I'm miserable, and no one's writing anything about me any time soon.

– You're young – give it time. Speaking of which, aren't you a little young to be working for Charlie?

She rolls her eyes. – Don't do it!

– Do what?

– The whole 'let's save the young prostitute' routine. Do you get off on it or something?

– I'm just concerned.

– Well, don't be! I've been looking after myself for a long time now, and I never needed some doughnut in a dress telling me what's what. I don't need no hero to look out for me – you get that?

– I got it.

– Good, now I gotta go – my ride's here, she says, pointing to the black limo pulling up to the curb.

I call after her. – Aren't you going to tell me your name?

– Candy, she replies.

– I'm Joe, I say, but she is already gone.

– *So, you've started chatting up little children, have you? I know it's been a while since you've got your leg over, but I didn't think you were that desperate.*

I was not chatting her up!

– *You were flirting!*

– I was not!

– *We'll see if the jury feels the same way.*

Forget about her. I want to hear about Novichkov's club. What have you gotten us into now?

– *Oh, you heard about that, did you?*

Yes, and I'd be interested to hear what you've got to say about that.

– *Not much to say. I saw an opportunity, and I took it.*

An opportunity that may get us killed.

– *Oh, fuck that drunken Russian faggot. He couldn't find his dick even if the way was signposted.*

And what about the money? Where is that?

– *It's a secret.*

Fine, be like that.

I take a swig of Dalmore and contemplate my next move.

– *Please tell me you're going home to change.*

That's right.

– *Good, because you really can't carry off that dress!*

Laura

It's coming. I know it is.

Any second now, that shitty email will be winging its way to my inbox. I brace myself, trying to untwist knots from my stomach. My heart thuds in my chest. I'm having full-blown palpitations.

I whisper a silent prayer, holding my breath as I click into my inbox.

Jesus wept – how are there twenty unread emails? I just checked it. I didn't realise twenty people in this company knew my name. Most people don't condescend to speak to the lowly HR girl – not unless they want somebody sacked, and they need me to do their dirty work.

I scan the senders' names and email subjects. My heart sinks. This'll take me hours. That's me working late tonight. Don't these idiots consider I might be entitled to some sort of life outside these four walls? Oh well, every cloud – I suppose that gives me an excuse not to tell Josh about the baby for another night.

No, Laura! You've got to tell him – and soon! How much longer can you keep it secret? It's already been two weeks. Don't you think he'll figure it out when you swell to the size of a house and need him to tie your shoes?

Maybe he won't notice the addition of a screaming baby to the apartment. He isn't exactly what you'd call observant. As long as he's got beer, his sofa, and football on the telly then he's happy as a pig in shit.

Anyway, I will tell him – eventually.

Just not tonight.

I'll tell him tomorrow. Yes, that's what I'll do. Maybe I should get him drunk first. He always handles bad news better once he's had a few drinks. Anyway, he might want to have a little baby – yeah, and pigs might fly.

You know what he'll say – 'we're not ready to have a baby' – 'we can barely look after ourselves, how can we possibly take care of some tiny helpless thing?' And doubtless, he'll find a way to blame me, even though he'd been the one who'd refused to wear the condom. Let's play Russian roulette he'd said, and now I'm the one shot with the bullet.

I scan my emails again. Still no sign of the email I've been dreading all morning, but I know it'll come sooner or later. It's inevitable – the meeting invitation my boss will be compelled to send.

I look at him through the glass wall of his office – sitting like Little Lord Fauntleroy in his ivory tower. He's wearing a bright red waistcoat, which screams alpha male aggression. Hey everyone, look at me – The Big Swinging Dick is here! As if anyone could miss him, with the amount of noise he makes, squeezing his ego-inflated head through the door each morning.

And then the email comes. The subject line screams at me: Presentation Practice Run Through.

Oh shit! Oh fuck! Oh shit!

Why is he doing this to me? Doesn't he trust me not to fuck it up? Or is he just inviting me into his office so he can criticise and tear apart everything I've written? I'm doing it for real in two hours – surely, it's too late to make changes now.

If he wanted to do a run-through, we could've done that last week. No, that would've been too bloody sensible, wouldn't it? Doesn't he understand I've got loads of other work to do?

I'm going to reject his meeting request.

Yes, I'm going to bloody well do it. I'm not going to stand for his shit anymore.

I move the cursor over the decline button.

My finger twitches above the mouse.

No more Walk Over Laura.

Today is the first day of the rest of my life.

Fifteen minutes later, and I'm stood in The Big Swinging Dick's office, running through my presentation.

His face gives nothing away the whole way through.

When I'm finished, he pauses and taps his forefinger against his lips.

– Not too bad, he eventually says before criticising the beginning, ripping apart the middle and rewriting the end.

– I don't have time to re-do the slides, I say, foolishly expecting him to agree with me.

– Of course, you do. They're only minor changes.

I nod my head in agreement, but deep inside, I'm fantasising about strangling him with the cord of his desk phone and beating him around the head with the receiver.

Now my stomach hurts, and I'm nervous – wishing I was anywhere but here, talking to this walking dildo.

My mind goes back to poor Lisa Traynor, who'd I'd read about in the newspaper this morning. How must she be feeling, not knowing if her little boy is alive or dead? That must be the worst of it – the not knowing. And now I feel guilty because I'm not sure if I want to keep the baby growing inside me.

What would Lisa say to me right now? Would she tell me to hold onto this little life and never let it go? Would she tell me not to worry about some pointless presentation? Focus on things that matter. Life shouldn't be suffered in an office, dying the death of a thousand deaths. I can't do this anymore. I need to get out of here!

I charge toward the door.

The Big Swinging Dick calls after me. – Erm Laura, where are you going?

– I'm going home!

– Home?

– Yes – back to bed. It's very nice there.

– I'm confused.

– Oh, bless you, Christopher – I'm resigning. It shouldn't be hard to spot.

– You can't do that. What about the presentation?

– Why don't you do it? After all, you're such an expert!

– You can't leave straight away. You've got a notice period.

– Yeah, I've thought about that and you can shove it!

He looks like he's living out his worst nightmare. It's immensely satisfying.

– What's gotten into you, Laura?

– It must be hormones, I say. – You know what us girlies are like when we're up the duff.

– You're pregnant?

– Yes, so for the health of my baby, I'm walking out of here right now!

– Well, I hope you're not expecting a reference.

– That's not very nice considering I was planning on naming the baby after you.

– What? Really?

– Yes, because that's just what the world needs – another Arsehole!

Jack

She looks about as pleased tae see me as a hairy wart oan a cock.

– Hi Mary, ah say.

Aam stood oan her doorstep wi mah shoulders hunched. Rain lashes down.

– Are ye gonnae let me in or let me drown?

– Don't tempt me! she says, movin aside, allowin me entry.

– So, what have we done to deserve the pleasure of your company?

– Ah thought eh'd check how mah girls are gettin oan.

– They're out, I'm afraid.

– Where? ah ask a little tae aggressively.

– Ray took them down the park. They should be back soon.

The mention ay Ray's name makes me want tae break somethin.

Ah follow her intae the kitchen. Everythin is shiny n new. Brushed chrome n marble worktops shout: 'look how much money a've got', just like the brand-new Porsche in the driveway.

– Would you like a coffee?

– This is unusual, ah say.

– What?

– This isnae how it usually goes. Normally, we have this whole routine where ye tell me off for turnin up unannounced.

– Would it make any difference? she asks, handin me a coffee.

– Probably not.

That's the good thing about bein a copper when you've been through a divorce n kids are involved. Normal visitation rights don't apply. What the fuck is Mary gonnae do – call the police tae kick me out? Good luck wi that!

– Sae, how is Gay Ray? ah ask.

– Oh Jesus, I've got better things to do than spend my Saturday than getting into a slagging match.

Unfortunately, I don't sae the next words from mah mouth are carefully chosen tae induce maximum slag throwin.

– Has he come out ay the closet yet?

– What did I just say?

– Ah just cannae believe ye left me for a gay man.

– How many times do I have to hear this crap? A) I didn't leave because of Ray – I left because you're an inconsiderate prick with anger issues. B) Ray is not gay – can you digest that?

– Have ye seen the way he minces around, wigglin his arse? Ah bet he even writes poetry.

– He does as a matter of fact.

– Yer kiddin?

– No, I'm not.

– What a shirtlifter!

– You never took the time to write me any poetry.

– I ne'er took tae shovin gerbils up mah arse either!

– You're being homophobic.

– Aam nae homophobic.

– You are!

– The word phobia intimates the presence ay fear. Aam not afraid ay poofs, ah just don't like em.

– Charming! I thought the police were trying to be more inclusive these days?

– If ye believe that, you'll believe anythin. I suppose that explains why you'd believe Ray isnae a screamin bender.

– Please don't call him that.

– Would ye prefer arse bandit, rectum ranger, chutney ferret, uphill gardener...?

– Very mature, Jack!

Aam nae exactly proud ay myself right now. Ah wish ah could stop mah mouth from workin, but unfortunately, it's nae attached tae mah brain. Every time ah come here, ah give mahself a lecture – behave yerself n act yer age, but it's nae easy tae see yer ex-wife n kids livin in another house wi another man. It hurts n what makes it more difficult is that ah still love Mary, despite the bitter divorce.

Why did she have tae become sae fuckin happy after leavin? She could've had the courtesy tae get fatter or uglier. But nae – she got slimmer, younger-lookin n even got a tan. Why did she have tae end up wi someone sae fuckin perfect? Someone who'd buy her flowers oan Valentine's Day n take the kids down the park.

Someone reliable.

The world never evolved by men bein fuckin reliable.

– If Ray isnae bent, then why does he speak like that? If he got anymore feminine, he'd have tae put a tampon in.

– That's not even funny, Jack. Your banter used to be much better, and besides, I happen to like the way Ray speaks. At least I can understand what he's saying.

– What dae ye mean?

– Your accent, Jack. It's so strong now, I can barely understand you. When we were married, you lost the accent. I swear you've become more Scottish since we split up. It's like you're putting it on.

Ah consider that for a moment n then reject it. – Aam workin oan a big case at the moment.

– Really, she says, feignin interest.

– Yeah, ah think ah might be chasin a serial killer.

– That's nice. She's noddin, but she couldnae be less interested. – Are you still on that diet?

– Maybe.

– I think you should stop. You don't look well. Maybe Ray should take a look at you when he gets back.

– Aam nae havin Dr Dickrider puttin his hands oan me.

– Fine, be like that.

– Be like what?

– An aggressive, ungrateful bore.

Ah've got an extremely witty n intellectual retort pre-planned, but a key hits the front door.

Ray opens it up n mah two girls scamper intae the hallway, lookin sae fuckin happy.

Another dagger tae the heart.

– Hello girls, ah say.

They both freeze like we're playin statues. Neither look thrilled tae see me.

– Arenae ye nae gonnae give yer dad a kiss?

They stay where they are. Joanna chews her bottom lip. Tae her, ah probably look like some emaciated, nightmarish creature.

Ray wheels in two pink bikes. Fuckin hell, aam missin out oan sae much. Ah should be teachin em.

The daggers just keep comin.

– Hello, Jack, he says. – I didn't know you were coming around. What brings you here?

– Ah came here tae spend time wi mah girls, nae that it's any ay yer fuckin business!

Ray holds up his hands as though aam aimin a gun at him – if only.

– Easy, Jack, I was just asking!

– Well ye can stop askin, cannae ye?

– Stop it, Jack! Mary says.

– Stop what? Aam sick ay bein made to feel unwelcome around mah own fuckin kids.

Joanna n Kim sense the risin aggression in the air, back away from me n crowd around Ray's legs.

Joanna tugs oan his corduroys. – Daddy, can we go and watch cartoons?

Ah scream inside, feelin like mah life has been written out in some tragic script – the flawed cliché detective wi the terminal illness n the estranged family. – What the fuck? ah say, barely containin mah rage. – Did ah fuckin hear that right?

– Please, Jack, not in front of the kids! Mary says.

Ah jab mah finger intae the chest ay the corduroy-wearin cunt. – Who dae ye think ye are? You're nae their dad. Aam their fuckin dad n nothin will ever change that, nae matter how many bike rides ye take them oan.

– Of course, Jack, I'm not trying to replace you.

Why has this cunt got tae be sae nice? Why couldn't Mary have got together wi a complete scumbag, who beat her n treated her like dirt? Someone who'd make me look reasonable n rational. Maybe then Mary wouldnae look at me like aam such a disappointment.

Ah want tae continue mah rant, but a coughin fit erupts in mah chest. It feels like aam gonna topple over.

Ray puts his hand oan mah shoulder, steadyin me.

– Are you okay, Jack?

– Get the fuck off me, ah dinnae know where you've been!

Ah slap his hand away, gamblin that ah willnae fall without his support. Sweat runs down mah back n vomit burns up mah throat, sae ah push past Ray, stumblin intae the driveway. Ah could probably make it tae the bushes but instead opt tae give Ray's Porsche a new paintjob.

When aam finished, ah wipe mah mouth n look back at mah ex-family. Their mouths hang open. Eyes are wide wi shock.

Ah, fuck it! What dae they expect from a flawed cliché?

BASRA. IRAQ

June 2004.

No, no, Tony Blair!

That's what they chant over an over. I can ear them filthy rag ead cunts from two streets over. Is that sposed to fuckin bovva me? Like I give a fuck if they slag off that smiley joker cunt. These Iraqi rats could strip im naked an pull a fuckin train on im right here, in the middle of the street an it wouldn't cause me no bovva.

They've been protestin outside the British consulate for almost two hours now. Must be over a thousand a' them cockroaches — cheerin an chantin, burnin Union Jack flags. If it were up to me, I'd blast every one of em. Let em exercise their right to protest with a hollow point through their eads.

I'm walkin fru the Southern part a' the city alone - sumfin we're told not to do, but I don't give a fuck. None a' these dune niggers would be stupid enuff to take a shot at me an if they do, well good luck to em, cos I'm ready to kill any cunt who wants to try it.

Fuckin ell, it's hot. It's all that Tony Blair's fault. I shouldn't be ere, sweatin my nuts off, surrounded by subhuman scum. Weapons a' mass destruction, my arse! These savages couldn't operate their own cocks, let alone a nuclear weapon. The only fuckin weapon a' mass destruction that Tony Blair needs to worry about is his wife's face. She could give Freddy Krueger nightmares.

I turn the corner. The wind blows sand in my face. Streets are empty — the buildins are blown to shit, reduced to rubble. Sweat runs down my back an flies buzz round my ead.

I ear screams. Turnin, I see a little boy runnin toward me. He's covered in blood. His clothes are torn an hangin off im. He tries to run past me, but I grab im. His eyes are wide with terror. He jibber—jabbers sumfin in Iraqi.

— Slow down, lad, I say. — I don't speak no dune coon, so you better slow down, so I can understand what you're sayin.

From my limited Iraqi, I fink he says sumfin about someone hurtin his family.

— Show me, I say, takin im by the and.

He don't want to come with me — he wrestles an fights to get away.

— I — elp, I say, or at least I fink I say in broken Kurdish.

That seems to calm im down.

He leads me to a small house down a deserted backstreet. I push open the front door an I'm hit by the stench a' death. I old the boy close an my rifle closer.

The boy's sister is still breathin, but she's been gang raped within an inch of her tiny life. His parents are dead an ave been used to redecorate the livin room. Blood is everywhere - smeared all over the walls, floors an halls.

The perpetrators back up when they see me, an my rifle pointed at em. One of em steps forward - his face is all pointed an rodenty. He looks at the boy the same way a crack addict looks at a fix.

The boy wraps his arms round my leg - his ole body trembles like a newborn chick.

The rodent approaches, lookin sheepish.

I lift the boy against my chest. — You mislaid sumfin, Corporal Spivey, I say, handin the boy over to im.

— Sorry, Sir, it won't happen again.

The boy starts yatterin an drivellin, probably beggin for his miserable life.

He screams when the first knife enters im.

Clay

– Ssssh it'll be all right.

That's what he says as he carves er up like a Fanksgivin Turkey, slowly workin the knife up from er naval, up toward er chest. He makes sure the sufferin lasts as long as possible an the whole time he's cuttin er, he strokes er air, whisperin patronisin reassurances in er ear.

What an evil cunt.

Gotta say, I love watchin Spivey work. He's like an artist, who only paints with deep an vivid reds.

Linton an his bruvva stopped wrestlin against their restraints four dead niggers ago. Now they're both cryin like a pair a' pussies, lettin out alf'earted pleas for the slaughter to end.

Fuckin pathetic – it's amazin ow so many so-called tuff guys dissolve into jelly when you start scoopin out their loved ones' insides.

I ask each victim's name an ow they know Linton before Spivey turns them into a canoe. So far, we're up to free cousins, five friends, free random hookers an a nephew.

Odessa, the girl with the black eye, who Spivey's currently cuttin, is apparently a friend, but I suspect Linton is fuckin er. I move to the next body in line – there ain't no need to ask er name.

– Ello, Chantelle, you remember me?

A muffled groan comes from behind the soiled underpants stuffed in er gob. Once upon a time, she'd been an attractive woman, but life with Linton ad taken its toll.

– I suppose you're feelin a little left out, I say, strokin er cheek. – Don't worry, you're next!

Chantelle shrieks an tears pour from er eyes.

When Spivey's finished with Odessa, he dumps er body with the others, then moves toward Chantelle.

– Please don't do this, Clay, Linton says. – Yuh leave er alone. She ain't got nuttin tuh duh wiv what appened between you an me. Yuh let her go an I'll make this right.

I try not to laugh at this fuckin hypocrite. Ow many times ad this worm wished this woman from his life? Ow many times had he treated er like shit? It's always the same story – we dunnt treasure fings that are truly valuable until they're about to be snatched from us.

– It sounds like you're beggin me, Linton. Is that what you're doin?

– Yea man, I'm beggin. I'll duh whatever yuh want – just let er go.

– You should remember, I don't do beggin! There ain't nothin worse than a pathetic piece a' shit beggin wiv piss in his pants.

To teach im a lesson, I instruct Spivey to cut Chantelle's nose off, before he guts er. It takes a long time for er to die an I make Linton watch every second of it.

– I suppose you're wonderin why I done this to you, Linton. You probly fink this is about revenge, but you'd only be alf right. After all, you really fucked me over, dinnt ya? I've had a long time to fink about all the fings I would do to you, but the truth is, I've killed these people for one reason an one reason alone: I want you to know how serious I am.

– Fuck yuh!

I wipe spit from his lips an smile at him. – That's more like the Linton I used to know. Welcome back to the land of men with balls.

– I'm gonna kill yuh!

– Save your threats. It's far too late to start playin the ero. Now I know you've got three million quid in your safe, so why don't you do yourself a favour an give me the combination before I become unpleasant.

– Yuh fink I care what yuh duh tuh me now? I'll see yuh in hell, yuh son of a bitch. Wah else ave yuh got? Yuh can torture me, yuh can kill me, but I'm not gonna tell yuh shit!

– You really do walk into these things, dunnt ya, Linton? I call my bruvva's name. – Benny!

Benny shuffles into the room, mumblin an gigglin to imself like a fuckin mong, still wearin that creepy Harry Styles mask, but I ain't complainin cos it's an improvement on his real face.

The whole mask fing was Spivey's idea. I told im we didn't need no masks for this job, but he'd insisted. Despite my reservations, I got to admit it's pretty funny.

Linton looks like he's gonna piss imself all over again when he sees Benny oldin his daughter's and – she's wearin a blindfold an got Spivey's headphones over er ears.

– She's got nothin tuh duh with this, Clay! Please nuh hurt me pickney.

– Yuh nuh chat tuh me inna yuh dodgy Jamaican patwah like some dry land tourist – you grew up in New Cross, ya cunt! Now give me that combination or I'll let my little bruvva fuck your little girl's brains out. Then when he's done, I'll take my knife an make a fuckin belt out of er. Now has anyfin I done since I walked into this house made you doubt a single fing I'm sayin?

– Please....please...

– You ain't fuckin listenin to me, are you? The combination! You give me that an I'll play nice. I'll even let the little bitch go.

– But yuh won't, will you? Yuh'll kill her if I tell.

– Why? She ain't seen our faces an them headphones are noise cancellin so she ain't eard no names neither. It ain't er fault, er father's a greedy, backstabbin little cunt, is it? You give me that combination an I give you my word she'll survive this.

– An how do I know yuh'll keep it?

– I gave you my word once before – a long time ago. I told you, if you ever fucked me, I'd come for you. Well guess what – here I am! You've got three seconds to start talkin. One...two..

– Okay...okay. I'll tell yuh... I'll tell yuh..

Linton's brother pipes up. – Don't tell him yuh fuckin......

I spread Carl's nose across his cheeks.

– Now you was sayin, I say to Linton, who sings like he's in the Vienna boy's choir.

Spivey disappears from the room, returnin a few minutes later wiv a dumb smile on his boat.

– Fuck me, Clay, there's more than we thought. I reckon he's got five or six mill up there.

– Fuckin ell, you've been a busy boy, ain't ya, Linton? You've been livin the igh life while I've been rottin in a cell.

– I told yuh what yuh wanted to know. Now yuh let her go!

– I gave you my word an I'll keep it. Benny, let the girl go.

My bruvva lets out a squeal an pulls er close. – No, she's mine, he says. – You promised I could have her. I want her! I want her!

– I dinnt promise you nothin, you retarded fuck! The man kept his word so now we gotta keep ours – let er go!

Benny shakes his head an backs away.

– Can somebody please get the girl away from the retarded paedo, please?

– I'll take her, Seth says, takin the girl by the hand, leadin er away.

Benny stomps his foot an sulks off.

– You see what I've got to deal with? I say to Linton.

– What are yuh going tuh do wiv us?

I open up my palm an show them the dice in my palm. – How about we leave that to chance?

Linton an Karl sob. They remember the dice. They remember all those times I used them – back when we worked together. They remember the blood. They remember the screams.

– Do you want to kiss em for luck?

They say nothin, so I roll – landin on two an free.

– Now I ain't gonna lie to you boys. One of you is gonna get it bad an the other is gonna get it really bad!

Gabby

What is he doing down there?

Is he trying to wind me up? That is his speciality after all – annoying the hell out of me until I reach breaking point. First off, he woke me by tossing and turning non-stop from 6 AM. Then he pulled the covers off me when he got out of bed, and now he's declaring war on some unseen enemy in our kitchen.

Doesn't he realise Sunday mornings are sacred? He should do – I've explained often enough. I look at the alarm clock on the bedside table. 8 AM. Yep, I should be sleeping now. I don't ask for much – the occasional cuddle, a nice bottle of red wine, and a lie-in when I have a hangover. Is that too much to ask?

Apparently.

Now, what is he doing – slamming cupboards, breaking furniture or is he perfecting new techniques in the art of sleep torture? Bastard! He could at least make me a cup of tea to apologise. That would earn him some redemption.

I listen for sounds that might herald the imminent arrival of hot liquid refreshment – a boiling kettle, a spoon rattle against porcelain, the creak of footsteps on the stairs – but there is none of that, just more clattering and clanging. And now what is this new noise indecently assaulting my eardrums? If I'm not mistaken, he's attempting to sing Time to Say Goodbye very unmusically.

I wrap a pillow around my head. Oh my God, he's gotten louder! How is that possible? Don't get me wrong, I love Ben dearly, but Andrea Bocelli or Sarah Brightman, he isn't.

Okay, now I'm pissed off and any chance of getting back to sleep has sailed off into the sunset, along with any appreciation I may have had for tenors and sopranos.

I jump out of bed, pull on my dressing gown, and bound down the stairs, ready for battle. He's going to suffer for spoiling Sunday snoozietime.

I find him in front of the stove, frying eggs and bacon. He'd better be making some for me, otherwise he'd better start running.

More than enough for two in the saucepan.

Damn! I was looking forward to telling him off. I clock the feast laid out on the breakfast table – croissant, smoked salmon, and orange juice. He's even put freshly cut flowers out in a vase. What's the matter with him? Maybe he's ill. Fuck! Now it's going to be difficult to give him a hard time.

Screw it! I'm still pissed at him for waking me, so let's get him.

– What are you doing down here?

– Making breakfast, he says.

– No, you're not – you're making a mess. You're supposed to put the oil in the pan, not spray it on the worktop.

He gives me a dismissive shrug that does little to lessen my irritation.

– Don't do that!

– Do what?

– Make out that I'm some nagging woman.

– Well, you are a woman, and right now, you are most definitely nagging!

– Only because you've woken me. What were you doing down here anyway – rearranging the furniture or something?

He points to the frying pan. – Don't you want any of this then?

I consider my response, not wanting to give him any sort of victory, but I'm pretty damn hungry, and this hangover needs to be remedied immediately with something greasy.

– I'm up now, so I might as well have something to show for it. It would've been nice if we'd had breakfast after a few more hours sleep.

– I just thought you'd be hungry given how much you were putting away last night.

– Me?!

This is another thing Ben does, which annoys me on a regular basis – convincing himself that I was more drunk than him when he was the one raiding the spirits cabinet when the wine ran out.

He was the one slurring and babbling bullshit, and now he's got the cheek to make out that I'm the alcoholic. Well, fuck that!

– I think you'll find that you were the one struggling last night, darling. Don't you remember me helping you to bed?

This is, of course, bollocks. There have been nights when gargantuan feats such as walking himself to bed would've been beyond Ben, but last night was not one of them.

Previous experience has taught me that even a small intake of alcohol will have seriously detrimental effects on my husband's short-term memory. He often fails to recollect events from the previous night's festivities – like that time he started singing Total Eclipse of the Heart at The Red Lion. He hadn't been bothered by the lack of microphone or accompanying music. Nor had he cared that it was quiz and not karaoke night – minor trivialities like that never seemed to bother Ben after he'd drunk enough to sink the Titanic.

I watch as he struggles to remember last night's events.

– I'm sorry, he says after a few moments of quiet contemplation.

I give myself a self-congratulatory fist bump. Well played, Gabby! I've heard relationship counsellors will urge couples to fight fair when domestic dust-ups occur, but they can get fucked. Little victories should be cherished – you never know when the next one will come along.

– Give me a hug, and I'll forgive you.

He wraps his arms around me and nuzzles my neck.

– What are you doing today? he asks.

– I'm going to visit Dad.

He pulls away from me, concern on his face. – Why?

– I'm going to invite him over for dinner this evening. It's been ages since he's seen Laura.

– I don't know why you bother.

– Because he's my dad and he should be here.

– You know he won't come.

– No, I don't know that because I haven't invited him yet.

– He always says no.

– Life is full of second chances, and I'm going to give him another one if that's okay with you?

– I don't want to argue. I just hate it when you come back from that place. It's like a little piece of you dies every time you visit him, and it takes you weeks to get over it.

I wish I could deny that, but he knows me so well. There's a huge part of me that wishes I didn't have to go today but I'm not ready did give up on Dad.

– Did you hear the weather forecast? Ben says, breaking a brief silence. – There's a hurricane coming in – a bad one.

I look out of the kitchen window, at the blazing sunshine and the cloudless sky. – Are you serious? It's the middle of August.

– Yes, it's some freak lightning storm. They were talking about it on the news.

– What is it with England? Even when it's hot, it bloody rains.

– I'll text Laura and tell her to set off early otherwise they'll get caught in it.

I let out a loud sigh.

– What's wrong? Ben asks.

– Nothing, I'm really looking forward to seeing Josh, I say with sarcasm dripping from my tongue.

– Not this again. I thought we agreed you were going to be nice from now on.

What was there to be nice about? Am I supposed to be happy that my beautiful, intelligent daughter is engaged to a smug, self-satisfied know all?

What in the world does she see in him? He isn't hugely attractive or remotely interesting. And why couldn't she find someone her own age? Not someone fifteen years older than her. Twenty-two is far too young to be getting married. She should be out enjoying herself, sampling all the fruits life had to offer.

She shouldn't be shackling herself to a man several notches beneath her on the evolutionary scale. I keep hoping she'll have a moment of clarity and realise her mistake, but she seems to be getting more infatuated with him.

– I don't know what you have against him, Ben says.

– I don't have anything against him.

– You're not a good liar.

– It's just when I imagined Laura getting married, I imagined her getting married to someone else – someone you know – better!

– You know things could be a lot worse?

On that I have to agree with him, things could be much worse. At least she's not pregnant.

Joe

– I think you've made the right choice – these will look lovely.

The old woman hands me the posies and grins, showing off yellowed teeth. I pay with mixed feelings, unsure of the ethics of her being here, standing at the cemetery gates, profiting from death like some soul–sucking demon.

I always tell myself to go to another florist, but I never do. It seems I'm willing to sacrifice morals for the sake of convenience. I suppose I shouldn't go for a few drinks at the Prince of Wales later either – what with Drew, the landlord offering a two for one discounted rate on wakes for those punters willing to share their bereavement with strangers.

I head through the wrought iron gates, under the watchful glare of stone gargoyles – their laughing faces are full of glee.

Mocking my pain.

Gravel crunches underfoot as I navigate the winding pathway through rows of headstones. A fellow mourner wishes me good day with a huge smile on her face. She's far too chirpy to be somewhere like this. I wonder who she's visiting – they must've been a complete tosser.

Part of me wishes I didn't have to come here. I'd do anything not to feel this pain, to feel this guilt.

I stop in front of the grey marble headstone. – I'm sorry I haven't been here for a while, Charlotte. I'd love to tell you that I've got a good reason, that I've been busy moving on with my life but that'd be a lie. You've got no idea how far I've fallen now you're gone. It seems you were wrong about me, after all. You were wrong to believe in me. You should've listened to them when they told you I was no good.

I feel foolish, talking to a pile of dirt and slab of stone. I know you can't hear me, Charlotte. I'd do anything to believe you could. If there were the slightest chance we could be together again, I would've closed the curtain on my shitshow life a long time ago.

Death is nothingness, an empty vacuum sucking up everything without pity or remorse. Perhaps I should be grateful for the absence of an afterlife. There's no guarantee I'd be going upward, that's for sure.

Beelzebub would probably roll out the red carpet for me, given all the dirty little things I've done.

What delights would he have in store for me? Fingernails down a chalkboard perhaps, or a spike up the jacksie? Maybe he'd do something truly diabolical like force me to sit through a Barry Manilow concert.

Please God – anything but Barry.

I kneel and tend the grave, removing dead leaves and remnants of posies.

I lay the new flowers.

Charlotte would've liked this spot, resting under the shade of the apple tree, listening to the chirp of bird's song.

She'd loved the outdoors and wide–open spaces, often talking about moving to the country – living in some cosy little village with a quaint pub – farmers sitting outside, discussing tractors.

– *But you put an end to that dream, didn't you?*

Of course, I did. Men like me don't move to the country and live happily ever after.

– *How do you know? You never tried, did you?*

No, I didn't. She didn't push me. She made sacrifices.

– *And how did you repay her?*

If I could go back and change it, I would. I would move out to that sleepy village, running through cornfields with barley between my teeth and a gay expression on my face. I would do all the things country folk do. I'd drink cider instead of beer. I'd do anything to make her happy.

– But it's too late now, isn't it? It could've been so perfect, but you ruined everything, just like you always do. Deep down, you know that you could've never made her happy because the only thing you're good at, is hurting people.

Get the fuck out of my head.

– She loved you despite your past, despite all your sins, but would she have forgiven you if she'd lived to see what you did?

That wasn't me. That was you.

– It wasn't bloody me – it was you!

I close my eyes and see the faces of all the people I've hurt.

They have so many questions.

Why me?

Fuck them – most of them deserved it.

– But not all.

One face stands out from the crowd.

– Do you remember how small he looked? Those tiny hands. You should be glad Charlotte died when she did. She would never have forgiven you for what you did!

What both of us did!

– Don't put that shit on me. That was all you, and you know it!

I fucking hate you!

– No, you hate yourself. Go on, read out what it says on her headstone.

CHARLOTTE QUINNELL.
DIED AGED TWENTY–SIX YEARS,
BELOVED DAUGHTER.

– Below that! What does it say below that?

I can't look. I can't say the words. Please don't make me!

– *Go on, isn't it about time you confessed to what you did?*

I take out my hipflask with shaky hands.

– *You can't drown the memory. You can't drown the shame.*

I fall to my knees – the smell of grass is in my nostrils.
– I'm so sorry, Charlotte. I failed you.

I get to my feet and walk away, making sure I don't catch a glimpse of the object to my right.

If I did, I might open my wrists from the shame.

CATFORD, SOUTH LONDON. 1979.

Benny makes a whooshing noise and dive-bombs the bathwater with his toy airplane. I'd like to play with it too but he'll scream his head off if I grab it.

– Mum, can we have some bubbles, please? I ask.

– Sorry, darling, but we don't have any. We'll pick some up tomorrow. Would you like that?

I nod. A lot.

The doorbell rings.

– I'll be right back. Watch your brother until I get back okay?

– Okaaaay.

Mum comes back but she isn't alone – she's with a strange man. I don't like him.

– Why don't you go into the living room and watch telly? Mum says to The Strange Man. – I'll probably be a few minutes getting them ready for bed.

– I fought you invited me around ere for dinner? Why did you invite me around ere so early if you wasn't gonna be ready?

– Sorry.

– Sorry ain't gonna cook my fuckin dinner, is it?

Mum looks scared. – I'll be another five minutes, and then I'll make a start.

– Why dunnt ya make a start now? I'll finish up ere.

– Are you sure?

The Strange Man nods and smiles.

Mum leans over the bathtub, kisses me on the head and leaves.

The Strange Man kneels by the side of the bath. He smells funny. – You dunnt like me, do ya, boy?

– No!

– An onest man, I like that. Why don't you like me? Is it cos I frighten you?

– No, I say, shaking my head.

Benny has stopped playing with his airplane. He looks worried.

– An why ain't you afraid a' me? The Strange Man asks.

– I'm not afraid of anything, I say.

– Is that a fact, tough guy? I fink you're lying. I bet you're afraid of at least one fing.

– Like what?

– This!

The Strange Man pushes my head under the water. I can't breathe. Water rushes into my mouth when I try to scream. Oh, Mummy he's going to kill me. I kick and fight to get free, but he's so strong. Oh my God, I'm going to die. Mummy – where are you, Mummy? Mummy, please save me!

He pulls my head out of the water and pulls me so close I can see the food stuck between his teeth. – That's ONE! he says, with a finger pointing to the ceiling.

Clay

Danny ain't nothin like Spivey, Benny, or that greasy little cunt Seth.

He's a gentle soul – that's what Mum would've said about im, God bless er. The lad ain't got a bad bone in his body an I suppose that's why I love im. It ain't easy for a man to say that about anotha man, specially if you're an orrible cunt like me.

– You know you're leavin DNA when you do that, right?

Danny wipes vomit from his mouth, eyes are waterin an bloodshot. He'd initially chucked while wearin his Will Smith mask, so right now he's wearin his lunch in his air, but he still looks cute as fuck. He could do wiv a shower though.

– I can't believe you did that, he says.

– Did what?

He points to Linton an Carl – they're both dead now – sumfin I'm sure they're eternally grateful for.

– Did that. How could you do that to another human being?

– That 'human being' got me sent down for eight fuckin years! Believe me, he ad it cummin!

– But how can you physically do that to someone?

– It ain't that difficult when properly motivated.

– Did I really have to watch?

– Sure did, we gotta toughen you up.

– I don't want to be toughened up.

I grab old of his arse an pull im close. – You're shakin, I say, strokin a stray air from his eye.

– Sometimes you really scare me, Clay. The things you do – they're not normal.

– An what exactly is normal? Normal ain't bein a millionaire an that's what we are now, cos a' me an my plan.

– But at what cost?

– You worried about gettin caught? Cos if that's what's boverin you, then you can cut that shit right now. You fink the police give a fuck about Linton or any of his crack dealin mates. They'll throw a party when they find out what we done ere.

– But that's not true, is it? You've killed women too – the police will come after us when they find out what you've done.

– What we've done, Danny! You may not've done the cuttin but you sure as shit dinnt do nothin to stop it. In the eyes of the law, you're just as guilty as me. Anyway, we'll be long gone before they find the bodies.

– You sure about that?

– Course, I am. We just wiped out Linton an his whole inna circle. You fink any of his street dealers know about this house? Even if they do, can you see em callin the cops? My guess is: these bodies will be left to rot for weeks until the stench draws the foxes in.

– What if you're wrong?

– Will you do me a favor an stop worryin?

I pull im close an kiss im on the lips.

Seth slithers up behind us. – I hate to break up you two lovebirds, but I think we ought to get out of here.

I let go a' Danny. – We'll leave shortly. Av you finished packin up the money?

– Yeah, it's all in the Range Rover. So, what's the plan now?

– We're gonna take a little ride into the country.

Seth screws up his face. – The country? What the fuck is in the country?

– An airfield, that's what – we're gonna catch a private jet an then we're gonna spend the rest of our lives drinkin cocktails an sunnin ourselves.

– And how are we splitting the money?

– You don't remember our arrangement? You get twenty percent.

– That's still the plan?

– Yeah, why not?

– I was worried you might stiff me.

– I gave you my word, Seth. You remember that? I always keep my word.

I look down on what remains of Linton, grindin my dice in my hand. Some people say revenge solves nothin an that it won't give you no satisfaction, but them people are full a' shit. I'm feelin absolutely fuckin great right now!

I follow the boys into the next room where we find Benny sat on the sofa, cryin his fuckin eyes out, cradlin Linton's little girl in his lap.

– What the fuck appened ere? I say, studyin the electrical cord wrapped around er throat. – I said, the girl lives.

– I did what I had to! Seth says.

I turn an face im. – Excuse me?

– She had seen my face. I must've been to this house a hundred times. She probably knew my name too. I couldn't let her talk to the police.

I touch my temple. I can feel a migraine cummin on.

– But I gave Linton my word. You eard that, right? I mean, you all eard it? I look at Danny an Spivey for confirmation. Both nod sheepishly. – So, I'm confused, if I gave the man my word then how come the girl is deader than a Chicken McNugget?

– I'm sorry, Clay, but she would've talked.

- I suppose you're right, I say, tryin to be calm, but deep inside I'm screamin *'ya slimy little cunt'*.

I touch the girl's face to one side so I can get a better look at the ligature. - At least you done it clean.

- I didn't want her to suffer.

- Well, looks like you got it bang on. I bet she was unconscious before she even knew what was appenin! See me, I couldn't eva get the hang of stranglin people. The ole fing could go on for ages an would get real messy. Here, let me show you!

Before Seth knows what's goin on, I've got the electrical cord wrapped round his neck, pullin both ends tight.

He claws at my arms with his nails, makin sickenin chokin sounds.

When his eyeballs roll back into his skull an it looks like he's about to pass out, I release the pressure, allowin im to breathe. His lungs rattle like a life support machine.

- You brought this on yourself, Seth, ya dumb cunt! I don't break my word for nobody!

When he's got his breath back, I pull the cord an choke the cunt all over again. I repeat the process five or six times.

Release. Tighten. Release. Tighten.

Eventually, I feel Spivey's hand on my shoulder.

- I think he's had enough, he says.

I look down at Seth - eyes pop out on stalks. - You're probably right, I say, twistin my forearms, snappin Seth's neck like a twig. His body goes limp an I lower im gently to the floor.

Danny looks in shock. - Why did you do that?

- He betrayed me an made me break my word. A man capable a' that ain't worth keepin around.

I ead outside, retrieve one of the duffel bags from the Range Rover an bring it into the house, before countin out piles a' money.

– Now, what are you doing? Spivey asks, lookin at me like I'm off my fuckin nut.

I pile the bundles neatly next to Seth's body an look up at im.

– I'm keepin my word.

Joe

I head to Darla's on Berwick Street.

It's a classy place if you're a pimp, drug dealer, or plastic gangster, but at least I can drink there for free. I'll never know how Charlie conned me into sinking my money into such a shithole. It'll make us a fortune, he'd said. Fat chance! Between my constant drinking and Charlie's handouts to so-called clients, we had barely broken even. Not that I give a shit about that now.

The business was Charlie's responsibility – I'd washed my hands of it a long time ago. All that matters is the bar stays open and keeps serving.

I hadn't even been consulted on the name change: Darla's – I don't know who Darla is or was. Probably one of the many dumb blondes Charlie had fallen in love with (and been rejected by) during our school days – back when Charlie had been a human being and not the blood-sucking parasite I had come to know over the last few years.

The doorman looks me up and down, giving me an icy glare, trying to assert his alpha-maleness.

Good luck with that prick! I've met far worse than you – the kind of men who inhabit the darkened recesses of nightmares. Men capable of terrible things – men like Mickey.

– *And men like you!*

What are you drivelling on about now?

– *Listen to yourself! You're pathetic – pretending to be whiter than white. Be a man and face up to what you are – what you've done.*

Not me. It was you!

– Is that how you sleep at night? Is that what you tell yourself? You need to understand there is no me and you! There is only us.

Fuck off out of my head.

– Ha! Try and make me.

I don't need to, I'll be balls-deep in Bourbon in five seconds flat, and then you'll be gone.

– But not for long. I'll never leave you! The voice chuckles to itself. *– Speaking of Mickey – do you remember what he did with that marker pen?*

Don't talk about that – I don't want to think about that!

Inside, the neon pink and black décor compliments the dried bloodstains. Clouds of cigarette smoke cloak the anonymity-seeking clientele.

I take a seat at the bar. Cristiano, the Italian barman, slides a double Jack Daniels into my hand.

– You better leave the bottle! I say to him.

– Charlie told me not to do that anymore.

– You know, Cristiano – you're just like a cunt but without the depth and warmth.

He leaves the bottle, and I sink the shot, immediately pouring myself another.

Then another – and another.

I'm lost in my own little world as debauchery unfolds around me. To my right, a group of Japanese suits snort cocaine and clap in unison as a teenage prostitute dances on their table. A big-breasted redhead in a leather catsuit straddles a sweaty overweight pig on another.

It's all rather depressing and I can't help thinking how much cleaner the world would be if somebody dropped a bomb on this place, wiping it off the planet.

Would anyone miss these people?

– Would anyone miss you?

I thought I told you to fuck off.

– I'm not going anywhere.

We'll see about that.

I take another drink, and the hunger in my stomach immediately dissipates. I must be halfway through the bottle when she walks in and sits next to me.

I barely recognise her – she's ditched the blonde wig she was wearing when we'd met outside Tierney's. Her long dark hair is pulled back into a ponytail, and she's swapped her trampy streetwalker uniform for stonewashed jeans and a loose-fitting white t-shirt. She looks like a fourteen-year-old Audrey Hepburn. And now I'm thinking, what did she do wrong in life to end up in a fuckhole like this?

I must be staring, because now she's staring back at me with an unimpressed look on her face.

– Can I help you with something? she asks. – I know they say it costs nothing to look but let me tell you that's not the case with me!

– Don't you recognise me? We met the other day – remember?

She smiles. – Oh right – Not Charlie's Brother, wasn't it? Sorry, I didn't recognise you without the dress. You know you ain't bad looking when you ain't got that shit plastered on your face.

– Funny, I was just thinking the same thing about you.

– Cigarette, she says.

– No, I brought my own this time, I say, holding up my Marlboro Reds.

– I wasn't offering, I'm taking! You owe me four cigarettes!

– I owe you three cigarettes.

– Ain't you heard of compound interest?

– Yes, of course – I'm just surprised you have.

– Are you calling me thick or somethin? Come on – four cigarettes, now!

– You can't be serious!

– What did I just say to you, Not Charlie's Brother? Nothing is free in this life. Now come on, cough em up!

I take out four cigarettes and hand them to her.

– Joe, I say.

– Excuse me?

– My name is Joe.

– My condolences, but I think I prefer Not Charlie's Brother.

– Is there any reason you're giving me a hard time?

– Yes, it's my night off, and I'm a complete bitch when I'm not being paid to be nice to you weirdoes.

– 'You weirdoes?' You're putting me in the same bracket as these freaks?

– Yes, for two reasons. One: you're here with said freaks and Two: last time we met, you was dressed in drag, eyeing me up and trying to ponce all my cigarettes. I rest my case.

– I was not eyeing you up!

– Yeah, you were – just because you were hiding behind the whole save the young–teenage–prostitute act, it doesn't mean you weren't being a pervo. Deep down under all the bullshit, all you men are the same. One day all us girls are gonna gang together and inherit the world, and it'll be all the better for it.

– I'll drink to that. I say, seeing off another double shot. How many has that been now? I've lost count.

– Can I get you a drink? I ask her.

– So now you're trying to ply an underage girl with alcohol? You're sending my weirdo detector into overdrive.

– I'm just being friendly.

– And I'm winding you up, Not Charlie's Brother. You need to lighten up. I'll have a Vodka Lime and Soda.

– How about I just fill a glass with piss instead? It'll probably taste better. Why not try a proper drink?

– What – like Jack Daniels? My dad always said bourbon was for men who couldn't handle proper whiskey.

– And where is your dad now?

– Don't try and gain insight into my troubled upbringing with amateur psychoanalysis. I'm here because I want to be, that's all you need to know.

I nod and order her drink.

– So, what should we drink to? I ask.

– Here's to those who've seen us at our best and seen us at our worst and can't tell the difference.

– I like that, I say, as we clink glasses and drink.

– You forgot to take it off, she says.

– What do you mean?

– That ring on your finger – you haven't taken it off. You got rid of the makeup and the dress, but you're still wearing that diamond ring. And the way your face just changed makes me think that ring has got a story.

– There is a story, I say, but she's no longer paying attention to me. She stares at something over my left shoulder – something that has scared the colour from her face.

I follow her gaze to a darkened corner of the bar, where a group of men sit, watching us with cat-like eyes.

A bald-headed monster makes his way over, dragging his knuckles along the floor. Candy's body wrestles with itself, torn between fight and flight. The brash tough street kid act drops, and the scared teenager is laid bare.

She stands her ground.

Good girl.

The Monster is now upon us – his whole head and face are covered with tattoos. He looks like a tattooed penis in a suit.

– Candy, we missed you the other night, he says. – You disappearin really upset the boss. Why don't you come over and apologise?

– I'm not working tonight. Please leave me alone.

– Don't be like that, girl. We'll make it worth your while.

He takes out a thick roll of notes.

– I told you, I'm not interested.

– The choice is scarcely yours, he says, grabbing her by the arm, pulling her from her stool.

I put my hand on his shoulder. – I'm so glad you're here, would you be a lifesaver and get us a bottle of your finest champagne, please? This should cover it, I say, tossing a fiver in his face.

– Are you tryin to be funny? he asks, roid rage veins popping from his temples.

– I'm sorry! I merely assumed you were the waiter.

– Oh, so you're a funny man. I wonder if you'll still be funny when you're sucking your dinner through a straw.

– You're quite right. How silly of me! Who in their right mind would hire a waiter as ugly you? They say beauty is in the eye of the beholder, but you really are something to behold. You didn't just fall from the ugly tree, you hit every branch on the way down and got a good pasting with the ugly stick when you hit the ground. What do you think, Candy?

– If my dog had a face like his, I'd shave its arse and teach it to walk backwards.

The Monster grabs me by the lapels of my leather jacket. – What the fuck did you say?

– Ugly – and deaf! Fuck me – you got it bad, didn't you? Are you sure you want to make it worse with a broken arm?

– You all right, Phil?

One of the Monster's associates has joined us. He's almost as ugly as his friend and could possibly provide a missing link between humanity and dog shit.

– This tough guy reckons he's gonna break my arm.

– Now that's not friendly, is it?

I reckon it'll be another five seconds before out and out violence breaks out and I'm painting the walls of this place with these cunts.

One.

Two.

Three.

Four.

Two other men come over from the table – they're wearing made to measure suits and are several notches higher on the evolutionary scale than their companions.

– What seems to be the problem here? one of them asks. He stinks of old money and gives me a look that makes me want to pop out his eyes and use his head as a toilet brush in a dysentery ward.

– Your ape was bothering my friend, I say. – I don't have time for sex pests, especially ones as ugly as him.

Old Money smiles. – I think there has been a misunderstanding, Candy and I are old friends.

– Is that right, Candy? Are you and Mr. Silver Spoon best buds?

– No!

– So, I take it you don't want to leave with this inbred mutant?

– That's putting it mildly.

– Looks like you've got your answer then, mate. Now please fuck off because you're eating into valuable drinking time.

Old Money couldn't look more fucked off if I'd wiped my cock on his suit. This man isn't used to the word 'no'.

– I think Candy might want to reconsider and you might want to think about how you address me in future.

– And I think you should fuck off before something breaks, namely my foot on your arse.

Old Money points to the man at his left – everything about him screams Special Forces, from his ramrod posture to his thousand–yard stare. – Allow me to introduce you to the head of my security, Mr. Gibbs, a former member of

Her Majesty's SAS and bodyguard attached to Sheikh Sultan Bin Mansour.

– Wasn't that the bloke who got his head blown off? I ask.

– After my time, old boy, Gibbs says, smiling.

And now The Hunger screams in my ear. – *Do it.*

What are you on about now?

– *Do it! You know you want to!*

I honestly have no idea what you're talking about.

– *You were thinking about popping his eye out. Go on – do it! It'll be fun, just like old times.*

Shut up!

– *Temper! Temper! Here's a fun fact: did you know that it only takes three pounds of pressure to pop a man's eye from his skull?*

If you know, then I know, dickhead.

– *So why don't you do it? Imagine super–tough SAS man rolling around on the floor trying to put it back in. He'll be screaming and crying like a little girl. It'll be the funniest thing ever!*

Yeah, hilarious. Are you quite finished?

– *Sorry, was I rambling?*

I'm trying to get us into a fight, and you keep interrupting.

– *Carry on – don't let me stop the good work.*

Now I'm back in the real world and Charlie, flanked by meathead bouncers, has appeared from nowhere and squeezed himself between me and Old Money.

– What seems to be the trouble here? he asks.

Old Money jabs his finger at me. – It seems Candy has a new employer!

– I am so sorry, I can provide you with plenty of other girls. We have a new girl, Francesca – you'll like her, she's part Italian.

– I trust she will meet our usual stipulations.

– She's perfect, Charlie says, leading Old Money toward the exit with an arm around his shoulder.

– Good, then you'll send her to the usual address in an hour!

– Of course, Charlie says, shaking Old Money warmly by the hand.

Why is Charlie crawling all over this guy? If he got any further up this bloke's arse, he'd be licking his tonsils. I've never seen him suck up to anyone like this before.

When Old Money and his goons are gone, Charlie charges toward me.

– What are you trying to do to me? Don't you know who that is?

– No, and I couldn't give the slightest fuck either.

– You may not give a toss about this business anymore, but I do! That guy could have this place burned down with everyone in it! Why don't you do me a favour and get out of here before you fuck up anything else?

Charlie is genuinely scared, and Charlie doesn't do scared. He was a man who'd made it his mission to piss off anyone, no matter who they were, so how come he's so scared of a toff in a Saville Row suit? It didn't make sense.

Who was Old Money and what did he want with Candy?

I stumble out of Darla's and into the night. How long have I been in that shithole?

I hear the hurried patter of footsteps behind me – a soft hand slides into mine.

Candy smiles up at me. – So where are you taking me? she asks.

Joe

– You know you'd be better off eating the packaging for all the good that burger's doing you!

Candy stops chewing her Big Mac and rolls her eyes.

– That's rich – getting health advice from a man who drinks whiskey like water.

We've been sat in Charing Cross McDonald's for thirty minutes, and I'm in awe of Candy as she troughs through the menu. For something made of skin and bone, she can certainly eat.

– So, are you going to tell me what all that was about back there?

– What was all what about?

– That business back at Darla's.

– Oh, that was nothing.

– Didn't look like nothing. You looked scared.

– I don't get scared.

– Could've fooled me – looked like you were about to use your underwear as a temporary latrine.

– Is this how you usually flirt on a date?

– We are not on a date!

– Why's that? Are you gay?

– I am not gay.

– Are you sure?

– Pretty sure, yes.

– You don't sound sure. You know it's okay to be gay. You can tell me. I won't tell anybody.

– Can we be serious for a moment?

– I am being serious. Quite frankly, I think you must be gay if you don't want a piece of this, she says, wiggling her bottom provocatively.

– You're what – fifteen?

– Seventeen actually.

– Yeah, and I'm the Queen of Sheba.

– I think we've conclusively established that you are a queen!

– Are you in some kind of trouble? If you are, I might be able to help.

– I can look after myself.

– Well, you've been doing a pretty good job so far. That's why you're turning tricks for Charlie Quinnell, a man who thinks scruples are a sexually transmitted disease. I hate to break it to you, Candy, but girls in your profession rarely walk off into the sunset.

– Firstly, will you stop callin me Candy, cos it makes you sound like a right paedo – my name is Becky. Secondly, you're fooling yourself if you think any of us get to walk off into the sunset. We're born and we die. Life is just a clock ticking. It's just some of us get a few less chimes than others.

– Very deep.

– Hey, can I help it if I'm a realist?

– You don't want to tell me your problem?

– If it means so much you, I'll tell you, but you have to answer my question first.

– Shoot!

– What's with that engagement ring?

– Are you sure you don't want to ask another question?

– If you don't like the rules, you don't have to play.

– I was married.

– But not anymore?

– Did the *was* give that away?

– She's dead, isn't she?

– How can you tell?

– You've got that look – the sad-puppy-dog-grieving-husband look.

– That's good to know.

– Don't knock it – chicks really dig it. So, what happened to her?

– She died during childbirth.

– I'm sorry, I didn't know that still happened. What was her name?

– Charlotte.

– How come you wear her engagement ring?

– I'm not sure. I suppose, I wear it to remember her.

– That can't be healthy – I mean, how can you move on if you're reminded by your ex every five minutes?

– Maybe I don't want to move on.

– I think you should – in fact, I think you should give it away right now.

– And who should I give it away to, exactly?

– How about someone like me?

– Someone like you, eh? I'll think about it, but I'm not sure I'm ready to part with it just yet.

– What happened to your kid?

– He didn't make it.

She reaches across the table and places her hand on mine. – I'm really sorry, Joe.

– *But she shouldn't feel sorry for you should she, Joey? You don't deserve anyone's pity...*

I pull my hand away slowly. – So come on, a deal's a deal. You were going to tell me how you got involved with that group of talking primates.

She crosses her arms defensively – she doesn't want to part with this story.

– Not much to tell. I've been working for Charlie for about two months.

– Lucky you!

– He might not be perfect, but he treated us pretty well.

– 'Us'?

– Yeah me and Nicola.

– Who's Nicola?

– My friend. We were both sleeping rough when one of Charlie's guys found us. He said we could earn some serious money. I gotta be honest – I never thought I'd turn tricks, but three weeks living on cold concrete will make you seriously re-evaluate your life choices. Anyway, everything was going well until the other night when Charlie comes to us and says he's got a job – some VIP willing to pay ten times our usual rate. Naturally, we were psyched and went for it. The car picked me up and dropped me off at some house in Knightsbridge.

– Where in Knightsbridge?

– I can't remember exactly, but you should've seen this place – it was swanky as fuck. So, I knock on the door, and it's answered by some freak in a tux. He shows me through to a room where there's even more freaks and a whole bunch of girls – and they're all really young – even younger than me! Nicola was already there. I knew something weren't right. I was getting this really weird vibe. These people weren't normal. Anyway, what really freaked me out was the look on Nicola's face. She looked terrified. It was like she had seen or heard something.

– So, what did you do?

– I got the fuck out of there. I went to the bathroom and climbed out the window. When I got outside, I phoned the police.

– Did they come?

– Yeah, I watched them arrive from across the street.

– And?

– And nothing! They went inside, then they came out and fucked off again.

– Maybe there was nothing illegal going on.

– Are you kidding me – a house full of paedos and teenage working girls? They were on the take. Fucking coppers – they're the worst criminals out there.

– What happened when the police left?

– These guys brought Nicola and the other girls out, bundled them into a van and drove off.

– Where were they were going?

– Fucked if I know.

– You know there's a chance the people in that house were just average paedos looking to get their leg over?

– That's possible, but there's one problem with that theory.

– What's that?

– I haven't seen Nicola since.

I try and tell myself that Becky is overreacting, but there was something about the way Old Money had looked at her. It was not a kind look. What would've happened if I hadn't been at Darla's? Was Charlie in on it? Had he arranged for those goons to be there and snatch her?

– I don't think you should go back to Charlie's tonight, I say. – It might not safe.

– So where am I supposed to go, exactly?

– I think you should stay with me.

She starts laughing. – I knew it, she says.

– What?

– I knew you fancied me!

Gabby

I drive along with Journey's 'Don't stop believing' pumping from the stereo.

I love this – navigating winding country roads.... lost in an eighties power ballad. Or was this song from the seventies? I can't remember.

Fuck! This'll bug me for ages. Maybe I should try some memory association – I'm a smart cookie, I can figure this out. I could even turn this into some sort of game. Yay! Huge fun. So here goes – think back. When was the first time I heard this song? It must've been back in 1981 at the Beaverbrook School Summer Dance.

Chris Wilkins asked me to dance and I accepted – not because I wanted to, or because I fancied him. I just didn't have the heart to embarrass him in front of his friends. He'd almost fallen over when I'd said yes.

And how did he repay my amazing act of generosity? He waited until Love Hurts by Nazareth came on, then he squeezed my arse and forced his tongue down my throat.

I got him back – with a knee to the groin and a slap that sent his milk bottle glasses flying across the dance floor (aka the school dining hall).

Everyone laughed their arses off while he stood there holding his cheek, trying not to cry. I had almost felt sorry for him all over again.

How did that make sense? I've always been like that – so eager to please, not wanting to hurt anyone's feelings. Dad had done his best to drive that out of me, to instil toughness, and it'd worked to a certain extent, but deep down, I've always been more like Mum – quiet and timid. How old was I back then – fourteen – fifteen?

Where had that time gone?

I check myself out in the rearview mirror – wrinkles and laughter lines everywhere. Come on now, Gabby – you're being hard on yourself – you know you look good for your age, but still, what happened to that small-town girl who was gonna catch that midnight train anywhere?

I've lived my whole life in the sleepy village of Greybrook – or the land that time forgot, as I'd called it in my youth. I'd dreamt of escaping for so many years – throughout my whole childhood. There had been a deep-seeded yearning to escape to the bright lights of the cities – maybe London or Manchester – anywhere sheep didn't outnumber people.

It was going to happen too. I was going to break the family tradition, shunning a life on the farm for a highflying career in finance. The date was set, and my bags were packed. Two days after my twenty-first birthday, I was moving to London. It was happening.

That's when I met Ben.

I had been working the late shift at the Lamb and Flag, and the bar manager, Dave the Dickhead, had offered to give me a lift home. On the way, he'd decided to pull over and feel me up. I pushed him off and fought my way from the car. He chased after me and who knows what would've happened if Ben hadn't pulled over, asking if I was ok. He was unlike anyone I'd ever met. Everything changed the day I met him.

When I found out he was moving to the area, I immediately cancelled my trip and we became close. Of course, I tried to convince him that we could have a future in London, but he'd had enough of the city.

He'd sold his soul to the stock market, and he was starting a new chapter in his life now he'd made enough money. I could understand that – a city boy wanting to get a midnight train anywhere. So, we decided to stay in Greybrook. At least the money Ben had earned meant I didn't have to work on the farm.

I often wonder what my life would've been like if Ben and I had never met. What if he'd carried on driving that night? Would I have been happier? I doubt it. For a start, I'd probably be the victim of a brutal sexual assault and I would've had to work for a living.

There was Laura too – our perfect little daughter (although some of the choices she's been making recently are from perfect).

It's a real shame she's marrying Josh. I suppose he's kind of good looking in a not so obvious way, but I can't understand what she sees in him.

I pictured her marrying a doctor or a lawyer – someone who could provide for her. I don't have anything against police officers per se. They provide a valuable public service, but I don't think this particular police officer is good enough for my Laura.

I remember the row we'd had when she had called, telling me that she was engaged to that smug arsehole.

I wasn't pleased, to say the least. She'd burst into tears and said things like – *you don't know him like I do* and – *why can't you just be happy for me?* You know, the kind of vomit-inducing guff you hear in a Hugh Grant movie.

Eventually, I conceded that I might grow to like Josh – in fifty or sixty years perhaps. Ben had hardly helped – I'd looked to him for support, but he wasn't having any of it. Just let her be, he said – she's a grown woman, who can make her own decisions. No, she bloody isn't – she's my little girl, and she'll do as she's bloody well told!

Ben always takes her side. He's the one who gets to play the cool parent, and I'm the tyrant queen locking the

princess in the tower. He'd pissed me off this morning too
– telling me not to bother inviting Dad this evening.

Both Ben's parents had died in a car crash when he was
young, so he didn't understand my devotion to Dad.

My hands tighten around the steering wheel when I see
the sign up ahead, advertising McColl's nursing home for
the elderly.

I hate Dad being in this place. He should be living with
us, but he'd refused. In hindsight, that was probably for the
best – my marriage might not have survived Dad moving
in.

Ben and Dad never got on.

Dad had been suspicious ever since they'd first met, but
then he'd never trusted anyone who wasn't born within a
five-mile radius of Greybrook.

Why is this random Londoner trying to steal away my
little girl?

I take a right into the courtyard, and my heart sinks
when the tall white mansion comes into view. It's an
impressive building surrounded by tall oaks and willow
trees.

I park near the entrance and climb stone stairs to
reception, where I am greeted by Cheryl, the eternally
cheerful receptionist.

– Your father is in the garden, she tells me.

I nod and continue into the main lounge where the air
tastes of disinfectant mixed with dust and decay. Eyes
follow me as I pass tables and wheelchairs occupied by
lonely residents.

I make my way into the garden. I don't need to look for
Dad – I know exactly where he'll be. He's like Sheldon
from that annoying US sitcom – always in the same spot –
sitting on the bench, next to the rose bushes.

– Hello, Dad, I say to him.

He turns and looks up at me. – Hello, Gabby, how are you, my dear? Come and sit down. Tell me what you've been up to.

– Nothing exciting, I'm afraid. You know how Greybrook is – nothing happens there.

– Hmmmm, I've just been sitting here thinking.

– About what?

– Your mother. It's the scent of these roses, you see. You remember how she was, don't you? Always tending to those bloody roses in that garden of hers. Rose by name, rose by nature, I suppose.

– Yes, I remember. I was wondering if you wanted to join us for dinner this evening? Laura's coming over and she's bringing her fiancé with her. Do you remember Josh?

– Hmmmm hmmmmm.

He's no longer listening to me – just gazing off into space. I may as well be background noise.

– So, what do you think?

– About what? he asks, breaking his trance.

– Coming to stay at ours this evening. I'm making shepherd's pie – made from real shepherds.

– I would love to my dear, but I can't, I'm afraid. You see, I'm expecting my daughter any moment, but thank you so much for the invitation.

I feel like I've been punched in the gut. I should be used to this by now, but the pain gets worse every time we have this same conversation. Is there anything crueller than dementia? To watch your loved one deteriorate, until there's nothing left but an empty husk.

I hold his hand, listening to the tweet of birds, enjoying the scent of the flowers, wondering how many times I'll be able to visit him before he deteriorates further – before he is gone. We'd rowed constantly when I was growing up. He was a strict disciplinarian who'd been tough on me – always claiming I'd grow to appreciate the strength and resilience he drummed into me. I'm not so sure about that. I just wish we had more happy memories.

I stand and kiss him on the forehead. – Goodbye, Dad. I love you! I'm sorry if I never told you that enough.

He doesn't respond – his eyes have glazed over. He's staring out over the lawn again.

I turn and make my escape – desperate to be out of this haven of impending loss.

Soon, I'm back in the car and balling out my eyes, allowing myself five minutes self–indulgent wallowing before starting up the ignition.

The radio bursts to life. The DJ warns about the impending storm.

I hear a gentle tap on the windscreen.

It has started to rain.

Jack

– Where are ye at wi the Bella Hopkins investigation?

DCI Brannin looks up from his coffee. Nostrils flare.

– Haven't you got anything better to do than crawl up my arse? he asks.

– Nae presently.

– Okay, I'll tell you where we're at: we've got a dead girl minus a head – what else do you want to know?

– Ah want tae know if you've got any clues or suspects – ye know actual police work.

– Don't try and be funny, Jack, it doesn't suit you.

– Suspects!

– We're trying to locate her pimp – some lowlife called Eddie Marcowitz.

– Snakeskin Eddie didne kill her.

– Oh, really, Sherlock, how'd you know that, eh? The guy's got form for GBH and pimping.

– A pimp wi a record for violence n pimpin – you've really got this case cracked.

– So, what's your thinking then, genius?

– Ah told ye before, you're lookin for a serial. Buryin yer head in the sand willnae make the problem go away.

– Oh, a serial killer is it, Jack? Maybe Jack the Ripper is stalking the streets of Soho once again?

– Jack the Ripper was Whitechapel, shit for brains.

– Whatever – I'm just glad you're here to advise me. I mean the whole serial killer angle is far more plausible than this being an open and shut case of reprisal gone wrong.

– Are ye kiddin me? Her head was severed from her body.

– I read the coroner's report!

– A've worked vice for fifteen years n a've ne'er seen a pimp dae anythin like this. The girl was his product. She was how he got his livin.

– I know how the whole pimp – prostitute relationship works.

– Ye could've fooled me.

– Look – maybe she pissed him off.

– Pissed him off? What did she dae tae deserve that?

– Maybe she was gonna do a runner, he found out about it and wanted to send a message.

– What message – if ye don't like your head, come n work for me? Aam sure he'll have all the girls queuin up.

– Okay then, answer me this smart guy – if it ain't Marcowitz then how come he's done a runner?

– Eddie's missin?

– Had it away on his toes. No one's seen or heard from him since the night Bella disappeared. Doesn't sound like the actions of an innocent man, does it?

– Maybe he figured he'd be locked up first n questions asked later.

Brannin leans back in his chair, strokin his beard. Arrogance oozes. – There's one thing I don't understand about this theory of yours – correct me if I'm wrong, but don't serial killers usually follow a pattern? Gacy raped boys, then he strangled them. Peter Sutcliffe hit prossies with a hammer and left them in the street, but your guy hangs one girl, slices another to pieces, then he cuts another girl's head off. I don't see a connection other than the occupation of the victims.

– You're correct. Gacy n Sutcliffe had a formula – sae did Bundy n pretty much every other killer ye could name, but it was that formula that got them caught. This man is more clever than that. He doesnae want ye tae know he exists. He wants tae remain hidden in the shadows – that's how he's gonnae continue daein what he's daein.

– And you think the same guy is behind all these "disappearances" we've been having?

– Don't say it like these girls arenae missin.

– They aren't. It's a transient occupation – whores move from town to town. They go where the money's good.

– Nae without their belongings they don't.

– Where are they then? If they're victims of this mystical killer, how come we haven't found any bodies?

– I don't know – he must keep them or hide them.

– You're reaching, Jack!

Ah slam mah fist down oan his desk. Anger surges through me. Gotta get this arrogant prick tae listen somehow.

Now the whole office has gone silent. Eyes are all over me.

Ah hear whispers.

– Listen, aam tellin.... Now aam coughin intae mah hand. Blood splatters mah palm.

Brannin recoils, disgusted. – Jesus Christ, Jack, I don't want your disease. And would it kill you to have a bath – don't you have any self-respect?

The office bursts intae laughter. A voice shouts out.

– Yeah fuck off, Travis, you smelly bastard!

That sets off more mockin laughter.

The room spins – a glitterin mirrorball. Aam gonnae be sick. Oh God, please nae here – nae now.

Ah scurry from the room wi Brannin's words in mah ears.

– Ladies and Gentlemen, let's hear it for London's finest detective – Jack Travis!

Ah burst intae the lavvy – the cubicles must be fifteen paces away – there's nae way aam makin that. Ah head for the sink n chuck up all the colours ay the rainbow.

When aam done, ah splash mah face wi water n look in the mirror. Havin a good day, Casper?

The lavvy door opens behind me.

– Jack, are you okay?

Ah turn around. DI Nikki Cooper stares at me, concern all over her face.

– Aam fine, ah say. – Don't mind me. Besides, ye shouldnae be in here.

– Actually, it's you who shouldn't be in here. This is the Ladies.

Ah take a step back, examinin mah surroundings.

Clean walls – check.

Non-diarrhoea splashed toilets – check.

Absence ay piss stinkin urinals – check.

Feminine hygiene product dispenser mounted on the wall – check.

– It appears you're right, ah say.

– Told you, I didn't make DI by sleeping my way up the ranks.

Nae she hadnae.

She could have – easily. Nikki was an attractive woman who'd been propositioned by many senior officers, many ay whom had wives n kids waitin at home.

She hadnae wanted tae know. She'd made Detective Inspector on the back ay hard work n damn good policin.

– You know you can talk to me, Jack.

– What do ye mean?

– I want you to tell me what's wrong.

– What's wrong? There's a killer out there preyin oan little girls n no one seems tae give a toss – that's what's wrong!

– That's not what I meant, and you know it. I want to know why you almost dropped dead just now.

– It's nothin, ah huvnae been sleepin well.

– Is that the best you can come up with?

– It's all a've got.

– Well, when you feel like talking you know where to find me.

She steps forward n slides her arms around me.

What is she daein? Cannae she hear the silent bell ringin?

Unclean! Unclean!

She smells sae good. Her perfume is intoxicatin. It takes me back to that Christmas party when she'd gotten pissed n eh'd walked her home. When we got tae her front door she'd kissed me oan the lips n invited me inside. She wasnae completely legless, but she was drunk enough, sae ah politely declined.

What was ah playin at? This gorgeous, intelligent woman wanted me but eh'd said nae. She must've been drunk or gone temporarily insane. What could she possibly want wi a waste ay skin like me, a man who'd shafted his marriage n estranged his kids?

Eh'd kicked mahself for days afterward. How could ah blow it sae badly? Eh'd thought about askin her out in the weeks after, but what if ah embarrassed her? What if ah embarrassed mahself?

Best tae forget about it n thank God I had.

Where would we be now if we'd ended up together? She'd have tae look after me – she'd be sleepin next tae this human coat hanger.

Ah pull away from her n charge toward the door wi mah head down, sae she cannae see the tears.

CATFORD, SOUTH LONDON 1980.

I never remember my dreams.

Bobby Willis, who sits next to me at school is always telling me about the weird dreams he has, but I don't think I've remembered a single one of mine.

Does that make me strange?

I open my eyes. It's dark.

Neon blue numbers blink on the alarm clock: 02:00:00. How come I'm awake? Usually, I sleep through until morning, ignoring my alarm until Mum shakes me, telling me I'll be late for school.

Something must've woken me. Is that a noise coming from Benny's room? I climb out of bed and step into the hallway.

The sound gets louder as I creep toward Benny's door. I turn the handle slowly and push it open.

The noise continues. Metal springs creak.

Benny's white eyes stare out from the blackness – begging, pleading. Now I see the black shape on top of him – it looks like a ghoul from one of my ghost stories.

– Get off my brother! I scream, running toward it.

The Ghoul lifts me by the throat and carries me back to my bedroom. I try and scream, but its hand is over my mouth.

Oh God, it stinks! Where have I smelled that stink before?

Warm smelly breath is in my ear. – So, who's the little spy, eh? Do you know what they used to do to spies in Ancient Greece? They used to burn their eyes outta their sockets.

A lighter ignites and a warm flame burns near my eyeball.

– What did you see? The Ghoul asks. – You didn't see nothin, did ya?

– No, I didn't see anything!

– Good! Cos if you did, then I'd have to burn you, your mother an your cocksuckin bruvva. Do ya want me to do that?

I shake my head hard as I can.

– Good, then you keep your fuckin mouth closed! You understand?

– Yes, I say.

– I'm not sure I believe you, so I better make sure.

The Ghoul puts the flame to my belly. Searing pain rips through me. I want to scream but fingers are down my throat.

Biting down, I taste dirt and blood, but it keeps hold of me, running the flame across my skin. Tears pour from my eyes. Please stop! I can't take anymore. Please!

The bedroom light goes on, and I hear Mum's voice.

– What's going on, in here?

The Ghoul pulls me to his chest. – He's havin a nightmare. His voice is different now – softer. – Isn't that right, Clay – you woz just havin a bad dream?

I pull away, looking up to see The Strange Man smiling down on me – the V of his middle and forefinger placed slyly on his chest.

Two! he mouths silently.

I look at Mum and nod. – It was just a nightmare, I say.

So, now I finally remember a dream. If only I could forget it.

Clay

Sulk sulk sulk sulk.

That's what you always do, ain't it? It's the same act you always pulled when we was kids, throwin a tantrum whenever you didn't get your way. Remember my eighth birfday – one a' the few occasions I actually got a present. It was only a yo-yo – an opportunistic feft from Sainsbury's durin an early mornin alcohol run, but that dinnt bovver me one bit.

It made a change from previous birfday gifts rangin from malnutrition an belt buckle beatins. You couldn't av wiped the smile off my face with a golf club. That yo-yo was my most prized possession in the ole world – until you clocked it!

Your eyes opened wide as saucers an then you said, you ad to av it. Our parents ignored you at first, but their resolve lasted one ear-piercin shriek an a foot-sized hole in the livin room door. They ripped from my grasp an ad in your ands before you could say retard.

We're drivin fru the English countryside an you've been sulkin ever since we left Linton's. I look at your reflection in the rearview mirror. You've got your legs hitched up on the back seat, thumb lodged in your gob.

– Are you sure you don't want your McDonald's, Benny? I got you an Appy Meal – your fave'rite.

His thumb pops out of his mouth with a sickenin slurp. – I told you, I'm not talking to you, he says.

– Look, I already apologised, dinnt I? You sure you don't want your Appy Meal – it's got a toy car in it. You like toy cars don't ya, Benny?

I old it up so he can see it. He gazes at it longingly – drool angin from his lips. I fink his resolve is about to break, then his face ardens an he slumps back into a strop.

– You told me I could have her. You should've given her to me!

– I couldn't do that, Benny. I gave the man my word. You eard me say that, dinnt ya? If a man ain't worth his word, he ain't worth nothin at all.

– But it's my birthday and I want a present.

– I know it's your birfday. That's why I bought you an Appy Meal.

For the record, it ain't his fuckin birfday, but if I challenge im I'll never ear the end of it.

– I don't want a Happy Meal – I wanted her!

–Well, I don't give a fuck what you wanted, you ungrateful cunt! You fink I like havin a retarded child molester for a bruvva? Let me tell you sumfin, I don't. You're nothin but a fuckin embarrassment to me. In fact, you're damned lucky I continue to look after you. Maybe I should pull over an throw your fat arse out the car. Would you like that? Then you could sulk by the side of the fuckin road an I wouldn't have to listen to you!

It feels good to get that off my chest, but I've made a huge mistake – Benny doesn't andle confrontation well an today ain't no exception – the tears come fick an fast – he makes a high–pitched whinin sound.

Spivey who's sat next to im, removes a headphone from his ear. – Clay, can you shut this retard up, or would you like me to sew his mouth shut?

– Hey, you don't talk to my bruvva like that an you don't call im no retard – you ear me?

– Well, he's doing my fucking head in!

– Still, you don't freaten my family – ever. Next time you talk to im like that, we got a problem.

Spivey slumps back in his seat an turns up the volume on his Ipod. Great – now I've got two girls sulkin in the back of my car.

I look over at Danny in the front passenger seat – he's got his back to me, starin out the window.

– An what's the matter with you? I ask im.

– Nothing.

– Don't give me that. I can tell you got a strop on. You gonna tell me what's wrong or I gotta beat it outta you?

– A lot of people died back at Linton's – did it really need to go down like that?

– Are you kiddin me? What woz I sposed to do?

– You didn't have to kill them.

– Don't you remember what that black bastard did to me? I did eight years inside cos a' that snitchin little bitch.

– But you didn't have to kill everyone else, did you?

– So, you want to be lookin over your shoulder for the rest a' your life? We just stole six million quid of unlaundered drug money – you fink that's the sort of fing people forgive? They'd have come lookin for us. All them cunts needed to die.

– It isn't right, Clay.

– What tha fuck did you just say to me? How fuckin dare you lecture me on right an wrong. I don't remember you complainin when I woz watchin your back inside. Don't you remember how much I looked out for you? If it woznt for me, you woulda been E-wing's steady bitchmeat. Your arsehole woulda been the size of a fuckin watermelon by the time they finished wiv you.

– I know, I'm grateful. I just don't like killing people.

I rest my hand on his thigh. – I know you don't, Danny. That's why I love you. You're so innocent. You're like the part of me that wants to be a better person. I don't know what I'd do if it woznt for you, but you gotta understand, I ad to kill them people. I did it for us. Now come ere an give us a kiss.

I grab im an pull his lips onto mine.

– Don't forget to keep your eyes on the road, he says, pullin away from me.

That makes me laugh. He's such a worrier.

I look back at Benny. He's still makin that awful noise, rockin back an forward like a loony in a padded cell. He'll be like this for hours. I'm not sure I can take it much longer. That's when I see somethin up ahead that might cheer im up an save me from stranglin im wiv his own intestines.

I pull the car to the side of the road an roll down the window. – Hey there, how are you doing? I was wondering if you could direct me to the nearest police station.

I don't listen to the directions that follow – I'm too busy thinkin how cute she looks in that school uniform.

Joe

I acknowledge this is creepy, and if she were to wake up, she'd probably get freaked out and leave, but I can't help it.

She looks so peaceful – I could watch Becky sleeping for hours. I wonder what she's doing on the streets. What was so bad that she would choose this life, falling into the hands of ruthless men like Charlie?

What was she running from? An abusive father or a domineering mother? It's cliché, but so often, it turns out to be true. I could always ask her, but I won't.

It's none of my business.

Whatever secrets she keeps are hers and hers alone. Maybe one day she might tell me, but I doubt it. She's so defensive – a real tough kid. She probably learned to bury painful truths a long time ago – to suppress memories best forgotten. We all have our ways of coping and learning to forget can be the best of them.

She opens her eyes, catching me gawping at her. – What the fuck are you doing – watching me sleep, you weirdo?

– Good morning to you too, I say casually, but deep down I feel like a Peeping Tom who's been caught with his cock out.

– What time is it? she asks.

– About half twelve. I was beginning to think you were never going to wake up. Next time you might want to try the bed in the spare bedroom.

– I like the sofa – it's comfy.

– Would you like some breakfast?

– Depends, what have you got?

– Only toast and orange juice, I'm afraid. She leaps up from the sofa and dashes toward the dining table, stuffing food into her mouth.

– So how long are you planning on keeping me here? she asks with a mouthful of marmite-covered toast.

– You're not a prisoner, and you know you can chew your food before you swallow?

– Am I not refined enough for you? Is that why you brought me here – so you can do your Dr Higgins routine?

– Dr Higgins?

– Yeah from Pygmalion – it's a play by George Bernard Shaw.

– I understand the reference. I didn't think you were a literary scholar.

– I see – because I sell my pussy for a living, I must be TAPS.

– TAPS?

– Yeah, Thick As Pig Shit!

– I didn't say that. It's just when we first met, you thought Les Miserables was an East London barman, and now you're throwing George Bernard Shaw at me. It's almost like you pretend to be 'TAPS'.

She shrugs her shoulders. – That's how you get the beating of people – when they underestimate you.

– So now you're letting me in on all your secrets.

– Not all of them, she says with a wicked smile.

– Anyway, you didn't answer my question: how long are you planning on keeping me here?

– Until I've found out exactly what you've gotten yourself involved in.

– I haven't got myself involved in anything. I probably overreacted. Like I told you, the police went into that house and then they left. They didn't arrest anyone, so they must've thought everything was okay.

– And what about Nicola? Aren't you worried about her?

– Girls move on all the time. For all I know she went back home.

– What about those men at Darla's. They didn't seem too friendly.

– I can handle those arseholes. I'm telling you there's nothing to worry about. Nicola is fine, and no one is after me.

– Perhaps you're right, I say, but doubt tugs at me. I pour myself an orange juice and sneak in a double shot of gin when Becky isn't looking.

When I turn around, her face has gone ghostly white and tears stream down her cheeks. She is reading the newspaper.

– What's wrong? I ask, looking over her shoulder at the full-page spread bearing the headline: 'Another Teenage Prostitute Dead'.

The article is accompanied with photographs of young smiling girls.

Becky is focused on one image. Her body trembles.

That's when I know I am looking at Nicola.

Gabby

To the rest of the world, Margaret Moriarty might appear to be a sweet, innocent old lady, but I know she's a randy old bitch. I'm sure she'd try and seduce Ben if she was thirty years younger or he was partial to necrophilia.

Ever since her husband, Horatio died three years ago, she's made it her mission to spend as much time in my house as humanly possible. She's always making goo-goo eyes at Ben, feeding him cakes, trying to make him fat.

I've just driven home from the nursing home to find them playing chess in the kitchen when all I want to do is flop on the sofa with a box of chocolates and feel sorry for myself.

– Who's winning? I ask, pretending to care.

– Ben is, Margaret says. – You're so lucky to have such an intelligent husband.

That makes Ben smile – he's such a pushover.

– I had a very good teacher, he says.

I think I'm about to throw up. Obviously, I don't hide my revulsion well, because Margaret looks like she's ready to stab me and bury me under my own patio.

– Why don't you take my place, Gabby? she asks.

– I don't know how to play, I reply. Something this crafty bitch well knows.

– Oh, of course, you don't, do you? I don't know how I forgot that. Maybe I could teach you sometime.

God, I hate her. I try and think back to when our animosity started.

We'd been friends once – back when Horatio was still alive. I'd loved that man. He was a larger than life character who could light up the room with his infectious personality and endless stories you'd heard fifteen thousand times before, but he had a unique skill for making you not care about that.

I still remember when he told us about the diagnosis – stage 5 prostate cancer. The brightness in his eyes was replaced by fear and he wasn't the same man. Things got worse when the chemo started. His hair fell out and his body wasted away.

Originally, Horatio hadn't wanted to do chemo because the doctors told him it was too late to save his life. But Margaret forced him into it. It might buy you some more time, she'd said. I'll never forget the last meal we had with them – the last time the four of us were together. Horatio spent the whole evening with his head down the toilet, while we ate, pretending everything was normal.

When it came to say goodbye, he'd been so apologetic with eyes full of fear, as though he'd known it would be the last time we'd see him in his own house – as if he could see that hospice bed calling out to him. I'd thrown my arms around him – he felt as though he'd break in two if I squeezed too hard.

Alas, that was my last memory of poor sweet Horatio – weak, skeletal, and half-dead.

And it was this bitch's fault. If she hadn't forced him into that fucking chemo, then I might have one last lovely memory of my dearest friend. I might have heard those stories one last time.

Margaret didn't take Horatio's death well. Hardly surprising given they'd lived in each other's pockets for sixty years.

She stopped looking after herself – she no longer ate or cleaned. It was like something had broken now Horatio was gone and her body was looking for an excuse to pack it in.

What else did she have to live for now? They had been unable to have kids, even though they'd both wanted them, and it wasn't as if she could start swiping through Tinder at the ripe old age of eighty-five.

That's when Ben stepped up and started looking after her. He took her to the supermarket and would pop over to her cottage every day, so she had someone to talk to. And now she'd taken to turning up at the house uninvited.

– Checkmate! Ben says, raising his hands victoriously.

– Oh, well done! Very well played. I didn't see that coming. You've improved so much.

– I'm sure you'll get me next time. Another match?

Oh shit, I think to myself. I really want this woman out of my house – now!

– Are you sure you have time for another match? We've got a lot to do before Laura gets here.

Ben looks at the clock on the kitchen wall. – We've got plenty of time!

– But I need you to get some wine from the cellar.

– How long do you think that'll take me?

I shoot daggers in his direction. – I'm sure Margaret would like to get off home.

– Gabby's right. You've both got things to be getting on with. I really should be on my way.

– I'll drop you home, Ben says, grabbing his car keys.

– You're so good to me. Gabby, I hope you realise how lucky you are!

– You shouldn't say things like that, Margaret, I say.
– He's got a big enough head as it is.

– Please give my love to Laura – it's been so long since I've seen her.

I watch out of the window as they drive away.

On the horizon, black clouds gather.

Clay

The schoolgirl looks absolutely terrified when Spivey drags er out the car boot. She wrestles against er wrist an ankle restraints, frashin like an animal caught in a trap. If it woznt for the gag in er mouth, she'd be screamin er fuckin ead off.

I take out my knife an old it against er throat – that gets er attention.

– Stop that right fuckin now or I'll ave to urt you. You want me to urt you?

She shakes her head an mews like a cat. I rip the gag from er mouth.

– Please don't hurt me, she says.

– What's yer name?

– Kkkk...irsty.

– I'm really sorry I gotta put you in this position, Kirsty, but I'm in a bit of a fix ere. You see that man over there?

Er eyes focus on Benny – he's got a drooly dumb look on his face an he's already sportin a huge erection under his dungarees.

– That's my bruvva, I say. – He finks it's his birfday today an if I don't get im a present, he's gonna make my life a livin ell. That's why I've gotten im you.

Now she makes an awful whinin sound.

– Come on, Kirsty, I fought we were past that. If you're not goin to behave then I'll have to discipline you.

I push my blade arder against er neck. She flinches when I knick er.

– So ere's what's gonna happen. My bruvva is gonna take you into them woods an what appens then is up to you. You can be a good present, or you can be a bad present. The good present gets to go home an do er omework, but the bad present – well, you don't wanna know what appens to the bad present. So, are you gonna be a good present?

She nods her head. Tears run.

– Good, cos if you give my bruvva any problems I give you my word, you'll regret it. You don't wanna face my dice.

Benny steps forward an sweeps er up in his massive arms. Kirsty's eyes bulge from their sockets – beggin an implorin. She reminds me of them flies I used to feed to that spider in my room when I was a kid. I swear them flies would stare right at me as the spider sank its fangs in – beggin me for help.

But I never did. I just stood there an watched as the fly fought against the inevitable, wings buzzin an flappin.

If Kirsty ad wings, she'd be buzzin too. I almost feel sorry for er as I watch em disappear into the woods.

– You're not seriously going to allow this to happen? Danny asks me.

– What d'you mean?

– She's only a kid.

– What the fuck is that sposed to mean? Age is relative – she's gonna get fucked by someone sooner or later so it might as well be today.

– Please, you've got to stop this!

– An listen to Benny whine for the next undred miles?

– It's not too late, Clay.

I drive my fist into his gut. He doubles over, gaspin for breath. Then I hit im in his side. He curls into a ball on the ground as I kick im in the ribs over an over. He squeals like a little piggy.

– Please, no more! No more!

I drag im to his feet, bendin im over the car. - Now you listen to me, you little cunt! My bruvva is gonna fuck sumfin on his birfday. Now it can be that little bitch or it can be you. He don't normally go for blokes, but I'm sure he'll make an exception for one as pretty as you. So, who's it gonna be - er or you?

- Her - it'll be her.

- That's a good boy, I say, rufflin his fick curly hair. I love im when he's like this - so weak an vulnerable. If Spivey weren't watchin, I'd fuck im right this second.

I pull im close an whisper in his ear. - I'm so sorry, Danny. I don't know why you make you insist on makin me so angry. I just want the best for you - for us. You do know that, don't you?

- Yes, Clay.

- An you ain't ever gonna leave me, are ya, Danny?

- No, he sobs.

- Good, cos you're mine now. You belong to me. That's what you promised when we woz in prison. You ain't gonna forget that, are you?

He shakes his ead. I ope he's tellin me the truth. He'd made me the same promise when he was released from Belmarsh. He gave me his grandma's address an told me he'd wait for me.

When I got out, I went to the house an found it empty. The neighbour told me that the old bitch ad died an Danny ad sold up an fucked off.

It took me ages to track im down, but I eventually found im walkin along Brighton peer with some dumpy fat slag.

I'll never forget the look on his boat when he clocked me an Spivey - looked like he'd shat imself.

- We're engaged! The fat pig proudly declared, showin off a diamond sparkler on er finga.

Danny begged me not to urt er, so I gave im my word I wouldn't if he came back to me. He agreed but free days later he came to me in an awful state – jitterin an mumblin.

Apparently the pig's mum ad rung im, sayin the pig ad been missin for two days. He asked if I had anything to do with er disappearance.

No, I assured im. I couldn't believe he could even stoop so low to ask me that – after all, he should know, I always keep my word.

Laura

– You should've discussed it with me first!

– What?

– Quitting your job. Don't you think it should've been a joint decision?

– You're not still whining about that, are you? It's been four days, you'd think you'd be over it by now.

Josh has been moaning for the whole drive. He always gets sulky when we're driving to my parents. So far, he's been taking delight in pointing out the rapidly diminishing bars of reception on his mobile phone. It's down to one now apparently.

– I just think you should have spoken to me. We do have a mortgage, you know. How are we going to pay it on just my salary?

– Something will come up.

– Oh, silly me for forgetting!

– You know how much I hated that job.

– Everyone hates their job. That's why it's called work.

– Well, maybe I want something better.

– Like what – a dole queue?

– No, you sarky git! I'm planning to work.

– Doing what exactly?

– Don't sound so sceptical. I have skills!

– Okay, Liam Neeson – I'm waiting.

– I'm going to be a food vlogger.

He takes his eyes from the road and looks at me as though I'm totally insane. – You can't just make up a job!

– You've heard of vlogging.

– Sure, I have, but it's not what I'd call a job.

– Yes, it is.

– Having a job involves making money.

– I will make money.

– How?

– You get paid for views and likes. He doesn't look convinced.

– So, you've given up a great job in London so you can post videos of yourself making food?

– I don't consider going to an office every day a great job.

– At least you could've had a career.

– Now you sound like Mum. I know I won't make millions, but I'll make enough. I just want to do something I'm passionate about. And besides, I want to work from home – I have a feeling that's going to be very important from now on.

I feel his eyes all over me. Be brave, Laura. If you can tell the Big Swinging Dick to piss off, then you can tell Josh about the baby.

– What do you mean? Josh says. He's staring at my hand caressing my belly.

– Okay, I need to tell you something, but you have to promise you won't get mad.

– Oh no! Whenever you say that, it's always followed by something really bad.

– Like when?

– Like when you bought that cat.

– I wouldn't say that was really bad. Anyway, I thought you'd grown attached to Mr. Tiddles?

– In your dreams!

– How come I caught you cuddling up to him on the sofa?

– He may have fallen asleep on me when I was hungover, but that doesn't mean I've developed affection for him.

– Yeah yeah – lie to yourself if it makes things easier.

– Okay, so what is this terrible thing you have to tell me? Your mother isn't moving in, is she?

Be brave, Laura. Be brave.

– I'll tell you but remember that you're driving. If you take your hands off the steering wheel to strangle me, we'll swerve off the road, crash into a tree and die in a blazing inferno, so you've got to promise not to get mad.

– Okay, I promise.

Here we go. World War Three, here we come. – I'm pregnant, I say, sucking in a deep breath and waiting for the nuclear fallout. But it doesn't come. He just stares ahead, looking out onto the road.

– Don't you have anything to say?

– I'm thinking, he says.

– About what?

– About walking around with a little mini-me and how nice that'd be. Yeah, I think I could get used to that.

– You're not mad?

– Mad? Why would I be mad? I think it's the best thing ever. I lean over and kiss him on the cheek.

– I love you, you know!

He gives me a cheeky smile. – You're not so bad yourself, he says. – But there's only one problem.

– What's that?

– You do realise your mum is about to kill me.

Clay

Benny emerges from the bushes – his face is bright red an he's blubbin like a baby.

Blood runs from his eye an part of his left eyelid hangs off. I don't need to ask what appened – I know the story before he tells it.

– What appened, Benny? An where's the girl?

– She scratched me and ran away.

– What tha fuck d'you mean, 'she ran away'? The little bitch was tied up! How could she run anywhere?

– I untied her.

– An why did you do that, ya dumb cunt?

– She said she wanted to give me a cuddle.

– An you believed her, you fuckin mong? You're repulsive – our own mum wouldn't want to cuddle you, so why would that little bitch be any diff'rent.

– I don't know...I..

– You don't know? Well that's all right then. I always knew you woz a fuck up, but this is a new low.

– I'm sorry, Clay, he mumbles, drool runnin from his mouth.

For a moment, I forget about the big fucktard in front a' me, an I fink about the boy I'd known when I woz little. He'd been sweet an sensitive, but that was before The Ghoul ad moved in – before the beatins, the sodomy an that night when everythin went really bad....

I put my arms around him, ignorin the stink of body odour. – I'm sorry, little brother. I know it ain't your fault. You're a retard, but I still love you – you know why?

Because we're family an there ain't nothin more important than that.

– I'm sorry, Clay, he says again.

– It's okay, I tell im. – Now I need you to fink ard now. This is really important. I need you to tell me which direction that little bitch went.

Joe

– Surely this can't be the smartest thing to do! Becky says.

– What do you mean?

– Well, you don't bring the mouse to the cat, not if you want the mouse to live anyway.

– You are many things, Becky, but I don't think I could ever describe you as a mouse.

– No, at this precise moment, I feel more like a worm on a hook. Why have you brought me here?

We're parked up in a rented red Mini, staring out of the windscreen at a huge mansion on Curzon Street. It took three hours driving around Knightsbridge before Becky eventually spotted the place. She hadn't been lying about its grandeur – there was serious money here.

– You didn't answer my question – what are we doing here?

– Being curious – don't you want to know what happened to your friend?

– I already know what happened to her and so should you. We both read the same fuckin newspaper. Someone hung her from a building – remember?

– And don't you want to do something about it?

–What are we gonna do? Are we going to go all Deathwish on these guys or something?

– Deathwish?

– Yeah, you know that old movie with Charles Bronson. It was on TV the other day. I couldn't have less of a clue what she's going on about.

– I don't watch TV.

She looks at me like a twelve-inch cock just grew out of my forehead. – You don't watch TV? So, what do you do in your spare time?

– I drink. I thought you had noticed!

She stares at the silver hip flask in my right hand.

– What's the deal with that? You trying to kill yourself? Cos if you are, I could totally help out with that.

And now I'm giving her the funny look.

– Excuse me?

– The way I feel about you right now – for bringing me here, I could happily beat your fucking brains in!

– Well, thank you.

– No problem. So, are you?

– What?

– Trying to kill yourself?

– I am not.

– You could've fooled me. You know my dad drinks?

– How would I know that?

– You could've guessed, I suppose. I mean the odds must've been pretty good with me being a whore n'all.

I cringe. I've never liked that word. There is something obscenely dirty about it. Pro, hooker, working girl – not exactly nice, but at least they don't have your ears screaming out for soap.

– You're not a prostitute. Not anymore. You're never going back to that life.

– Okay, so what am I going to do then?

– We'll talk about that later.

– What's wrong with right now?

– We're working *right now*.

– This isn't working. This is trying to get me killed.

– You're not going to get killed.

– I hope not, because I've grown attached to my body. I don't want it strung up or decapitated – thank you very much.

– I wouldn't put you in danger.

– Errr newsflash, those sadistic fuckers are probably looking for me right now and thanks to you, they're not going to have look very far, are they?

– Haven't you heard of hiding in plain sight?

– You what? That is without a doubt the dumbest thing I've ever heard.

I open the car door and step out of the Mini. – Wait here.

– Where are you going now?

– I'm going to take a closer look.

– You can't leave me here!

– Stay put and you'll be fine.

I close the door and cross the road.

The house is more impressive up close, surrounded by wrought iron fences, complete with pointy-ended spikes and barbed wire. I count fifteen mounted security cameras pointing in every direction. The level of security surrounding the house is insane and has been installed by a professional. Probably that arsehole Rudd – the super tough SAS man who'd gotten in my face back at Darla's.

– *You should've popped his eye out, you fucking pussy!*

I reach for the hipflask in my inner jacket pocket. Not there. Fuck! Must've left it in the car.

– *You'll never get rid of me. I'll always be here. With you.*

I look up at the windows.

Tinted.

Someone has spent a lot of time and money, making sure everything that goes on inside stays private. It's not really a house. More like a fortress. The occupants are either ridiculously paranoid or up to something really bad. What horrors have happened in there? It wouldn't be easy to find out without being seen, which is a shame because I'd love to take a peek inside.

– *I can get you inside.*

Please fuck off!

– *Be a man! Just scale the fence, march up to the door, ring the doorbell and then whoever opens the door – pop their eyes out their skull and snap their fucking neck!*

Thank you for that, but we need to be more subtle.

– *Subtlety is for queers.*

Suddenly I hear a voice, and it isn't the one emanating from inside my head.

– Can I elp you wiv sumfin?

I turn and see a repulsive toad with a shaved head glaring at me through the iron railings.

– I'm looking for number thirty-six, I say.

He gives me an untrusting look. – This is number five. Thirty-six is down the other end of the road. Are you simple or sumfin?

– My mistake. Thank you for your help.

– No problem – blind cunt!

I ignore the remark, but The Hunger is less forgiving.

– *You gonna take that from that maggot? You know what I would've done to that ugly prick. I would've....*

Popped his eyes out? Yeah, I got that.

I head back to the Mini – smoke and a God-awful sound comes from the open window.

– What are you doing? I say to Becky, who lies across driver and passenger seats, smoking while playing music at full blast from the radio.

– I'm hiding in plain sight, she says.

Becky shuffles over and I sit behind the wheel.

– What is this dross you're listening to? I ask.

– This is Bon Jovi. Don't you know Bon Jovi?

– I don't listen to music.

– You don't watch TV and you don't listen to music? What kind of freak are you?

– *Yes, Joey, what kind of freak are you? Don't you think you ought to tell her?*

I take a swig from my hip flask. The whiskey burns as it goes down. It feels good.

Now the DJ reads the news headlines. He focuses on one story: Multiple bodies discovered at a house in the country. The investigating officer makes a statement – he sounds shaken, intimating a level of brutality beyond your average murder scene. It takes a lot to rattle a senior Detective Inspector, so now I'm curious, wondering what they found. The suspect or suspects are still at large and extremely dangerous.

– Oh, my God! That sounds terrible. What's the matter with people? Becky says. – I hope they find the bastards and string them up.

– Yes, I agree, but The Hunger is in my ear.

– *Sounds like something you would've done back in the day, doesn't it?*

I take another swig of whiskey.

Becky stares at me, concerned. – You know, you shouldn't drink and drive – it's really dangerous.

I start up the car and give her a wink, before pulling away.

– So much for keeping me alive then! she says.

.

Joe

I drop Becky back at the flat and then head to Charlie's office at Tierney's.

He smiles when he sees me. – So, what brings you here today? You planning to fuck with more of my clients or are you looking to steal more of my whiskey?

– I want you to tell me about the house on Curzon Street.

The smile disappears from his face.

– What house on Curzon Street?

– Don't play dumb with me.

– Who told you about that?

– Becky told me.

– Becky?

– Candy to you!

– Somebody should really explain the meaning of client confidentiality to that girl. Where is she anyway?

– You don't need to know.

– So, she's at your place then? You never were a very good poker player.

– You need to forget about her, Charlie. She's not on your payroll anymore.

– Is that a fact?

– It's scripture.

– I don't appreciate people barging into my office, telling me what's what. That girl is my property. You don't get to tell me what I do with my property.

– You mean like Nicola? I toss the newspaper on his desk, open at the page with Nicola's smiling face. – You recognise that girl?

– No – should I?

– You're not a great poker player either, Charlie. I know this girl worked for you.

– I have lots of girls working for me. You think I know them all by name? Why do you think I employ pimps?

– You should remember this girl. Her name was Nicola – you sent her to that house on Curzon Street and now she's dead!

– You should forget about that house, brother. No good will come from asking questions about that place.

– Why? What is it, Charlie?

– I told you! Don't ask fucking questions!

– What are you afraid of?

– I'm not afraid of anything!

– Could've fooled me. Fear's pouring off you like sweat right now! And you certainly don't seem too bothered that someone killed your property. The Charlie I worked with would never have stood for that, so now I'm wondering who owns that house. Who could possibly be so bad they've got the terrible Charlie Quinnell pissing his pants?

– Augustine Webrich owns the house.

– The aristocrat?

– You've heard of him?

– The name's familiar.

– Well, let me tell you, this is not a guy you want to fuck with.

– What are you talking about? He's a toff. What's he going to do – bore me to death?

– You don't know this guy. He's not just any toff. He's dangerous and he's connected to every outfit in this city. You wanna do business in London, then you go through him or you end up supporting a flyover.

– So, you're working for him now?

– I supply him with girls – he likes the young ones.

– And what do you get in return?

– He's opened up other avenues for me. Prostitution and extortion are good earners, but it doesn't hurt to diversify.

– So, you're a drug dealer?

– No, I'm an importer. You should see the numbers we're talking about here.

– Your sister would be so proud.

– Fuck you! You think Charlotte would be impressed if she could see you now? Just because you've had some kind of epiphany and you're pulling hookers off the street, don't make you a saint. I remember the things you did, Joe, and they make me look like a choirboy.

– People change, Charlie.

– Not you, Joe. You think I don't know it was you who turned over Novichkov's club? How long do you think it'll take the old man to work it out?

– Novichkov's a fat fuck who's afraid of his own shadow.

– Maybe, but did you know he was kicking up to the Vorie V Zakonie? It's their money you stole, you dumb fuck! I hear they sent a group of psycho torturers over from Siberia to get it back.

– I honestly don't know why you're telling me this.

– I hope not, because otherwise, you could have lots of trouble coming your way.

I get to my feet and head towards the door.

Charlie calls after me. – I know you think you're invincible – ripping off old fuckers like Nikolai Novichkov is one thing but Augustine Webrich is a whole other world of pain. There's something seriously wrong with that family. You're not gonna do anything stupid, are you?

– Me? Never!

Jack

Soho. The land ay the lost. The realm ay the forgotten. Beneath the glitz n glamour ay neon lights another world exists – a world ordinary people pretend nae tae see, where a fourteen–year–old can be bought for a tenner.

Ah walk down Brewer Street wi hands in mah pockets, wary ay pickpockets blendin wi the crowds. I neednae bother. Most ay the wee shits know me n the rest can spot a copper a mile off.

What gives me away? Maybe ah just don't belong. It's strange coz a've always felt an affinity wi this place.

Ah may nae have suffered a lifetime ay abuse but a've been rejected more times than ah wish tae remember. Firstly, by the army, then mah family n now slowly but surely, the police were daein the same – treatin me like a leper.

Ah turn ontae Waldorf Street, passin doorways crowded wi huddled bodies. A young lassie looks up at me – she cannae be older than fourteen.

– Got any change, Mister? she asks.

Ah can tell she isnae turnin tricks or usin yet but it willnae be long. Ah give her a fiver n say a silent prayer but aam nae hopeful. The weak ones don't make it.

At the corner, aam greeted by streetwalkers ay all shapes n sizes, colors n creeds. Most ay them nod at me. A've arrested most ay them, but eh'd always been fair.

Ah realised a long time ago, ah was never going tae rid the world ay prostitution. It's the world's oldest profession, predatin the dawn ay civilization sae what chance did ah have?

Across the street ah see two familiar faces – Cecilia n Ebony lean against a wall, cigarettes hangin out their mouths.

– Jesus, Jack, you look like shit, Ebony says.

– You're not wrong, Ebs, Cecilia says. – He looks like somethin that crawled out of Night of the Living Dead.

– Or a dog's arse!

They both laugh.

– Thanks girls, ah say, resistin the urge tae smooth down mah hair n make mahself more presentable. – Can ah offer you ladies a cigarette?

They snatch them greedily.

– So, what brings you to our cosy little shithole? Ebony asks, lightin up.

– Ah was wonderin if ye girls have had any unusual clients recently?

– Just the usual freaks.

– No one especially violent wi any weird fetishes?

– Are you kiddin me? Most of the freaks who come around here are into some weird shit. Why are you asking?

– Ah think there might be someone in Soho preyin oan young workin girls.

– Well duh! Open your eyes – there's always someone preying on us.

– Aam not talkin about punters or your pimps. Aam talking about somethin else – somethin worse.

– You're talking about the dead girls, aren't you? Cecilia asks.

– And don't forget the ones who've gone missing, Ebony adds. – Are you here to warn us, Jack?

Ah nod mah head. – That's right.

– Maybe, you should've warned that girl on Rampart Street.

– What dae ye mean?

– You ain't heard? Some girl was just snatched.

– When did this happen?

– I dunno – about half-hour ago.

Ah turn n run toward Rampart Street like a man possessed, bobbin n weavin through the crowds. They mutter n curse under their breath as ah push past them – a walkin scotch bottle calls me a wanker, but ah don't give a shit. A've got tae get tae Rampart Street n find out what happened.

Don't panic, ah tell mahself. This abduction might nae have any connection tae the murders. It's all in yer head, ye dumb fuck. When aam in spittin distance ay Rampart Street ah see the flashin emergency lights.

– Ye wanna tell me what happened? ah ask a spotty faced constable.

– A teenage girl was abducted about twenty minutes ago. Two men jumped out of a van and grabbed her right off the street.

– Ye get an ID oan the victim yet?

– Yeah – girl's name was Anne-Marie Towers.

– Fuck me, that was quick. How'd ye get that sae fast?

– Her friend saw it happen.

– Friend?

– Yeah, over there!

He points tae a wee lassie bein comforted by paramedics. She's visibly distraught. Tears run down both cheeks. Somethin is very wrong. She's wearin a super short miniskirt n got super slutty makeup trowelled oan her face, sae you'd be forgiven for thinkin she's a pro, but she doesnae have the toughness – the hard look girls got when they worked the causey.

Ah cross the street, flashin mah warrant card. – Ah understand you're a friend ay the girl who was taken?

She nods.

– Tell me what happened.

She tells me everythin – how she n Anne-Marie had bunked off school n gotten dolled up, hopin tae sneak intae a celebrity nightspot. She tells me how she'd seen two men wearin balaclavas pull her friend intae the back ay a van.

The last thing she tells me is Anne-Marie's age.

Fifteen.

Then ah simply say. – Fuck!

Laura

We pull up outside Mum and Dad's. It feels great to be back. I used to think this place was a prison when I was a child – when I had been desperate to escape to anywhere else – somewhere not stuck in the middle of nowhere, where you can get mobile reception and Wi-Fi isn't a distant dream.

Now with the benefit of hindsight, I realise the animosity I once held toward Greybrook was badly misplaced and that life in the city is not all it's cracked up to be.

Life moves too quickly in London. It's liberating to come back here where things move at a snail's pace – where people are friendly; they say hello in the morning and don't walk with their eyes fixed on the pavement.

I haven't told Josh yet, but I'm hoping we can move here in the future. No doubt, the suggestion will go down like a lead balloon, but who knows, maybe he'll surprise me. After all, he took the pregnancy much better than I expected. Surely, he'd recognise it would be better to raise a family where the air doesn't taste like you're sucking on an exhaust pipe.

I look over at Josh. He seems tense. – Are you okay? I ask.

– Not really. If I'm being honest, I'm dreading this.

– We don't have to tell Mum about the baby today. Would you feel better if we put it off?

– Yes, let's do that. Let's tell her when we're back in London – preferably over the phone.

– You wimp! I say, chuckling.

Mum must've heard us arrive because she's stood on the driveway waving to us.

Josh and I get out of the car.

– I've missed you, darling, she says, hugging me like she hasn't seen me for fifty years. – It must've been what – six months since I last saw you last?

– I was here two months ago, Mum.

She looks at me like I'm mad. – That can't be right, she says.

– Well, it is.

Mum shrugs. – Hi Josh, she says, not too enthusiastically, I notice.

We move to the living room, where Mike Oldfield's Moonlight Shadow plays on the vinyl record player. It's a song I'd been forced to listen to religiously when I was growing up.

– I would offer you some wine, Mum says. – But your father hasn't materialised from the cellar yet. I sent him down there fifteen minutes ago. God knows what he's doing.

– I'll go and check on him, I say.

– Yes, please give him a kick him up the backside for me.

I hear the start of an awkward conversation between Josh and Mum as I start down the stairs. It'll do them some good to spend some time alone. You'd find it hard to believe they were fully-grown adults – more like two stubborn kids in a playground, refusing to back down.

I find Dad sat on a wooden box, drinking straight from a bottle of Malbec.

– So, this is what you're up to, I say.

– Hello, Trouble, he says. – I'm glad you made it up here before the storm hit.

He offers me the bottle.

– Are you trying to get us killed?

– Your Mum won't know.

– What about red wine lips? If secrecy was your goal, you should've opened a bottle of white.

– There's no fridge down here and I don't do warm white wine. You should really try this though – it's very nice.

I take the bottle and pretend to have a swig. – So how come you're down here by yourself?

– Your Mum's on the warpath, so I thought I'd give her some space.

– She's always on the warpath.

– Don't be too hard on her. She went to see your grandfather today.

– I see – let me guess, he's not coming.

– No, he says, shaking his head.

– How is he?

– Not good.

We sit in silence for a few moments, passing the wine between us. I hope Dad hasn't noticed that the wine level doesn't drop every time I take a drink. I can see his mind ticking.

– You look beautiful, he eventually says. – That dress reminds me of the night I met your mother. She was wearing a dress just like that.

Ah, The Yellow Dress story.

Mum and Dad would often regale me with this tale over Sunday lunch. I must've heard it sixty thousand times before. They would tell me how Mum had been left stranded in the rain and Dad had stopped to offer her a lift. Then they'd fallen in love and got married within two months. I'd heard the story so many times, I'd grown to hate it, but now I'm afraid I might not get to hear it much more.

Both my parents are getting old now and that makes me sad. I used to love spending time with Dad when I was younger. We did everything together, but then we drifted apart. I stopped using the treehouse he'd built for my little friends and me. It had become dilapidated and overgrown with vegetation.

I no longer regarded Dad with starstruck awe and eventually stopped spending time with him. I know that happens in every child's life, but I wonder if he ever felt sad about that. Does he miss the time we spent together as much as I do?

Mum calls down from above. – What are you two doing down there? Do I need to send a search party?

– Oops, looks like we've been rumbled, Dad says, scooping up two unopened bottles of red.

We head upstairs. The smell of beef gravy and home-made Yorkshire Pudding wafts from the kitchen. Mum has an undeniable talent for cooking a roast.

– What have you two been up to? Mum asks, studying us like we're a pair of murder suspects.

– Nothing at all! Dad says, giving me what he'd class as a wink. He's never mastered the art – he always scrunches up his face like he's in pain.

There is a rumble of thunder outside. The house creaks as a strong wind blows.

The storm is finally here. I look out of the window as lightning illuminates the forest. Trees sway and bend in the gale, forging a path through the canopy. It looks like a huge monster is charging through the wood, trampling down trees, leaving a path of destruction in its wake. The wind picks up again, and the monster changes direction – now it's heading toward the house.

Getting closer.

A chill runs down my spine.

Clay

– Well, this is fucking shit! Spivey says, wipin rain from his face. – I'm absolutely soaking wet! I'm gonna kill that little bitch when I get hold of her. I'm gonna...

– Yeah, we get the fuckin point, I say. – Will you stop ya fuckin moanin, cos yer hurtin my ears!

Now Spivey gives me a look like he might actually stab me with that knife.

– Go on, try it ya weasely little cunt. I'll shove that blade up yer arse an turn into a fuckin seekh kebab.

Spivey's eyes narrow. – This is your fault, Clay. If you hadn't snatched that little bitch and left her in the hands of this spastic, then we wouldn't be in this situation.

– But I did, didn't I? We're in this shit now, so we gotta make the best of it.

– The best? We're lost in the fucking woods and it's pitch black. I can't see shit!

Spivey's right – as much as I hate to admit it. Rain lashes down like bullets, an the ground is a muddy bog. The wind owls fru the trees, leaves blowin all around us. Where did this storm come from? It just appeared from nowhere.

– We really need to get indoors, Danny says, rainwater drippin from the tip of his nose. He looks like a drowned rat.

– Clay, I'm scared, Benny says as a fork a' lightnin stabs the sky.

I put my arms round him. – I know you are, Benny. You'll be okay. I'll look after you.

Spivey glares at me. – Why the fuck are you being so nice to him? All he had to do was stick his dick in her, but he couldn't even manage that. We should just carve him and leave him to bleed out.

I grab Spivey by his jacket an spit in his face. – I told you earlier, you don't call him no retard an if you freaten him again, you'll be the one bleedin out.

– Stop arguing, you two! Danny says. – Maybe we should just head back to the car.

– Goin back to the car ain't an option, I say. – We've gotta find that little bitch before she blabs to the cops.

– Why don't we just head to the airfield? We can be out of the country before they find us.

– You fink any plane's gonna take off in this, you fuckin idiot?

– What if she's already found a phone and called the police? They could be on their way here right now!

– We just gotta ope that ain't so. Opefully, she's just as lost as we are!

– But....

– Shut it, Danny! I gave that little bitch my word that I'd get her if she fucked me over, so this is me keepin my word.

– So, we're gonna get ourselves struck by lightning or arrested because of your word?

– That's fuckin right, ya little prick! Now get movin before I break your fuckin nose!

We continue fru the woods – drivin wind an impenetrable blackness pushes us back. The heavy sports bags loaded with cash don't elp neiver. I'd been tempted to leave em in the motor, but what if the car was reported stolen or some cunt ad nicked it – then we'd be proper fucked. It woznt worth the risk.

Spivey stiffens an stops dead in his tracks.

– What is it? I ask im.

– There's something up ahead.

– What?

– Looks like a house.

Spivey's right. We've come to the edge of the wood. A small cottage stands in the clearin beyond – most of the lights are out, but a solitary candle burns in one window.

The rain pours as we approach – our feet squelch in the mud. The weather's so bad, I almost miss the girl–sized footprints on the pathway an can barely read the sign hangin on the gate.

It reads: Moriarty.

I knock on the door.

A withered an fearful voice calls out. – Who is it?

I do my best normal person voice. – I'm sorry to disturb you, but our car broke down, and we need to use your telephone.

– I'm sorry, I can't help you. The storm has knocked out my phone.

– Could we please come in anyway? It's terrifying out here.

– I don't think so. I'm an old lady and I don't know who you are.

I take a step back an kick the door, smashin the lock ta bits, sendin it flyin inward.

The old woman inside holds er hands to er face an shrieks. – What are you doing? You can't just break in here. You get out of my house right now!

– What will you do if we don't?

– I'll call the police.

– I fought your phone was out?

– You get out. You just get out of here.

I look toward the back of the house an see Kirsty escapin fru the back garden.

– Get after her, I say to Spivey.

– You leave her alone, the old woman says, blockin the way.

I grab er by the throat an squeeze so ard er eyes look like they're about to pop. – You wanna worry more about yourself rather than that witch. You should see what that vicious little cunt has done to my bruvva's face!

I look over at Spivey, wonderin why he ain't moved. Sumfin else has grabbed his attention – that black BMW pullin into the driveway.

Laura

No one expects the Spanish inquisition. That's what Monty Python said, isn't it? Well, I was expecting it and it's firmly underway. We've barely sat down to dinner and Mum is already in interrogation mode.

– So, how's work? she asks me.

– It's brilliant!

– That's good, she says.

– You weren't enjoying it, were you? Things must have improved.

– They certainly have. I try not to smile when the next words leave my lips. – I quit the other day, so things have improved immensely.

Mum stares at me like I've confessed to multiple murder. – Have you got another job lined up then?

– Nope.

– But you've got a mortgage to pay!

– We'll manage, Josh says.

Mum machine-guns him with her eyes. Josh might have been trained to take down criminals, but he's a pussycat when he's in a room with Mum.

– I expect you'll want us to pay, Mum says.

I'm determined not to lose my rag with her, after all, that's what she wants – that little nibble at the end of the line.

– We're not asking you to pay for anything.

– You can't pay for that fancy flat on just Josh's salary.

– How do you know how much Josh earns? Anyway, I've got some ideas.

– Would you care to share them?

– What's the point? You'll only mock me and say they're stupid.

– Is that code for: I don't have any ideas and I just threw away a good job for no reason?

– Maybe I don't want to spend the rest of my life biodegrading in an office.

– That doesn't sound like a plan to me – sounds like you don't have a clue.

Why is Mum being like this? Always crapping on my dreams. It's like she doesn't want me to be happy. Why is it so important to her that I have this highflying career? That was her dream, not mine. It had died when she'd fallen pregnant and decided to stay in Greybrook. Did she resent me for that? Maybe she's having a mid-life crisis, and there was me thinking they only happened to balding men with beer bellies.

– Maybe I don't want to have everything planned out, I say to her. – Maybe I want to be spontaneous.

– And are you okay with this? Mum asks Josh. This is a rhetorical question with only one acceptable answer.

He shrugs. – I'm happy as long as Laura's happy.

That was not the correct answer. Mum looks like she's about to throw up.

– And what about you, Ben – are you happy with this?

Dad's eyes open wide like he's a rabbit caught in headlights. – I agree with Josh. I think Laura should do whatever she wants to.

– Thanks, Dad.

– Am I the only one with any sense around here? You need to work Laura, or you won't make any money.

– What's the matter, Mum? Are you worried that I might actually be successful doing something creative?

Mum doesn't like that. Anger burns in her eyes. – And is there anything else you want to tell us?

I try not to think about the baby growing in my tummy, fearful that Mum may have miraculously garnered the gift of mind-reading. An awkward silence descends on the table.

– Well? she says.

– Well, what?

– Is there anything else you think we should know?

Oh my God, she knows about the baby! But how? I'm not even showing yet. I know because I checked in the mirror this morning and my stomach is flat as a pancake. Mum stares – piercing me with pale grey eyes.

I shift uncomfortably in my seat, glancing at Josh. He chews his food slowly, eyes imploring me not to do what he knows I'm about to do. He knows me so well. He knows how I respond when I'm challenged. There is only fight and zero flight. And now the words are flying from my mouth before I know what I'm saying.

– I'm pregnant!

A deathly silence sucks air from the room. Josh looks like he wants to crawl under the table and assume a foetal position.

Mum stares at me and I'm starting to wonder if she heard me at all. – I hope you're joking, she eventually says, shooting nuclear missiles.

– Don't be like that, darling, Dad says. – That's fantastic news, Laura. When are you due?

– I knew you'd take her side.

– This has nothing to do with sides. We're going to have a grandchild. I thought that was supposed to be a good thing.

– Our daughter is throwing her life away and that's a good thing?

– I am not throwing my life away, I say, rage boiling in my veins.

– You're only twenty-two, Laura. You're too young and immature to have a child.

– Immature?

– That's right – you can't even hold a job for more than five minutes. How can you think about raising a child?

– I'm a grown woman and I'm old enough to make my own decisions.

– Okay, you do what you want. What do I know? I'm only your mother. Why should you listen to me?

She gets up from the table and stomps upstairs. There might be a full-blown typhoon blowing outside, but it's far stormier inside this house. Now I wish I hadn't told her – not like that – out of spite and anger. What have I done? Me and my silly pride.

There is a flash of lightning that makes me jump from my skin. That was close to the house.

Too close.

The lights go out and now we're in darkness.

– What's going on? Josh asks.

– The power's cut out, Dad replies. – Must be the storm.

It may be dark, but I can see Josh's unimpressed face, which says: this sort of thing never happens in London blah blah.

Dad rummages through kitchen drawers. – Ah! Here we go, he says triumphantly, striking a match and lighting a candle. – Can you light up the rest of these? he asks, passing me the box. – I need to make a telephone call.

Dad jabs buttons on the phone, before replacing the receiver, grumbling under his breath. – Looks like the storm has knocked out the phone too, he says, pulling on his coat.

– Where are you going? I ask him.

– I'm going to see if Margaret's okay.

– Are you nuts? You can't go out in this!

– I won't be long.

– She'll be okay – that woman's tougher than she looks.

– I'm sure she is, but she's old and she's alone. I'll be as quick as I can. Will you tell your Mum for me?

– Why don't you tell her yourself?

– I'm not wearing my Kevlar vest.

That makes me laugh.

– You chicken! No wonder she thinks you two are having an affair.

– Don't you start!

I wrap my arms around him. – You be careful.

– Don't worry about your mum, he says. – I've known her a long time, and I know she'll be happy once she calms down.

– You wanna bet on that?

– She just wants the best for you.

I study his features. The warm candlelight accentuates his wrinkles, making him look older. He barely looks like the same man I'd idolised as a child. I kiss him on the cheek and tell him to drive safe.

Then he gives me one of his notoriously bad winks, then he's out the door, driving off in his black BMW.

Joe

The Webrichs are evil pieces of shit.

According to the book – The Silent Snake: A Horrible History of the Webrich Family, they have been one of the most powerful families in England since the sixteenth century.

The author, George R. Timbleton laid terrible accusations at their door, ranging from mass murder, witchcraft, and human sacrifice. He wrote about the unspeakable things, which had taken place at Webrich Manor – the family's ancestral home until it was demolished in a bombing raid during the Second World War – the only decent thing the Nazis had ever done, according to George.

The family sunk its claws into everything – the government, the military, and even the church. The first Webrich of prominence, Elias had been ordained as Abbot of Ashenridge monastery in 1521, but he'd been anything but a man of God. Locals from the town disappeared – many of them young girls.

Elias became one of the most feared men in the country and used his influence to acquire great wealth and huge swathes of land. He defied Henry the Eighth during the dissolution when the king ordered all monasteries in England be broken up and sold.

The King sent a battalion of soldiers with orders to burn down the monastery and put Elias in chains. When no word of their progress reached the palace, scouts were dispatched to Ashenridge, where the skins of the soldiers were found nailed to the monastery walls. The rest of the bodies were never recovered, and there was no sign of Elias.

He simply disappeared.

The monastery still stands to this day. I study the photo on page eighty-nine – the walls are charcoal black with huge pointed spires.

George suggests that although Elias would be long dead by now, his evil still lives on through his bloodline. Twin brothers Augustine and Tobias are named as the current incumbents of the Webrich evil empire.

I recognise Augustine from his photo. He looks exactly as he did at Darla's – smug and smarmy, oozing old money. There is no picture of Tobias, but he had followed his great ancestor's footsteps into the church until he had been defrocked ten years ago, following allegations of impropriety with homeless children. The claims were never conclusively proven as key witnesses disappeared before they could give evidence.

I look at the author's photo on the hardback's inside cover. The obituary beneath tells me of his demise – killed in a car crash two weeks before his book hit the shelves.

I close up the book and look up to see Becky staring at me from the sofa.

– So, what's this great plan then? she asks.

– Excuse me?

– The other day – in the car, you said, I wasn't going to be a whore no more.

– That's correct. And can you please stop using that word?

– So, what am I going to do then? It's not like I've got any A–Levels or anything.

– That is about to change. You, my dear, are going back to school.

Her face drops. Fear widens her eyes. I've seen this girl stand up to violent thugs – she's lived on the streets but mention the 's' word, and she's scrambling for cover.

– No fuckin way, she says. – I already tried that and it didn't work out so good. I think I'd prefer to go back to suckin cock for your brother.

– He's not my brother.

– Yeah yeah – whatever you say. But school though. Why do you want to put me through that? What did I ever do to you?

– Don't you want an education?

– For what? So, I can be like them stuck up idiots, working jobs they hate?

– You can do whatever you want. I just want you to have options.

– So where would I be staying while I was going to this school?

– You'd stay here.

Her eyes narrow suspiciously. Jesus, has anyone ever done anything nice for this girl in her whole life?

– And what would I have to do?

– Just the usual stuff – go to classes, do homework – you know the normal stuff other kids do.

– So, you won't be expecting me to parade around naked in my school uniform?

– How can you parade around *naked* while wearing a school uniform?

– It's a figure of speech.

– Yeah – a stupid one.

– Let me get this straight. You'd let me stay here rent–free, eat your food, drink your booze and you wouldn't expect anything in return.

– That's right. Well, everything except for the booze part. You're still underage.

– So, you're not going to try and hit on me? Jesus, what kind of fucked up pervo are you? That's the weirdest thing I've ever heard.

– It's weird to be nice to someone?

– Course, it is! The first time I met you, you were dressed up like a drag queen from Hell, and ever since you've either been pissed out of your skull or talking to yourself. Now you're offering me loads of free shit like a paedo handing out sweets.

– I don't talk to myself.

– Then who are you talking to?

– *Why don't you tell her, Joey?*

I move over to the kitchen counter, grab my Jack Daniels and swig directly from the bottle. – I'm not talking to myself. I'm talking to 'it'.

– *It?* What are you talking about? Are you saying you hear voices in your head?

– No, only one voice, and it's not just a voice, and it's not just in my head. It's like a hunger in the pit of my stomach that can never be satisfied. It wants to hurt people.

– And is this voice talking to you now?

– Yes.

– What is it saying?

– *Why don't you tell her, Joey? See what she does! What will she do when she realises just how fucked up you are?*

– Right now, it's telling me to rip your fucking head off!

Why did I tell her that? Was that me or was that The Hunger? That's the worst thing – I don't know where The Hunger ends, and I begin anymore.

I'm supposed to be protecting her from monsters like Charlie and the Webrichs, but here she is, locked away with the biggest monster of all.

I wait for her to run from the room in a fit of panic, but strangely she doesn't move – she just stares at me with a silly smile on her face.

– Oh dear, you really are screwed up, aren't you? I think me and you are gonna get on just fine.

Jack

– Are ye happy now, arsehole?

DCI Rick Brannin glares at me with hatred. – Did you have a brain transplant for breakfast or something?

– Ah told ye somethin like this would happen. I warned ye but ye dinnae fuckin listen.

– What are you talking about?

– Anne-Marie Towers.

– The missing girl?

– She's nae missin – she was snatched in the middle ay the street.

– And we're investigating.

– If you'd listened tae me in the first place, this whole god damned mess would never have happened.

– Hang on a minute – are you saying she's another victim of your phantom killer?

– That's exactly what aam sayin.

– I see. That's really interesting. So, he's moved on from prostitutes and graduated to schoolgirls?

– She wasnae dressed like a schoolgirl. He probably grabbed her n didnae realise his mistake until it was tae late.

Brannin shakes his head. – Please leave, Jack.

– Ye need tae act oan this.

– No, what I need is for you to get out of my face with this shit and if you ever pull anything like this again, I'll break your legs!

Chief Superintendent Morris enters the room with his face all scrunched. His nose is pointed up in the air like he's sniffed out a particularly fragrant fart. – What's going on here, Rick? I thought I heard raised voices.

– It's DI Travis, Sir. He's gone full loony tune on me!

– Sir, ah have reason tae believe there's a serial killer operatin in London n he's been preyin oan teenage prostitutes. Ah also believe Anne-Marie Towers may be a potential victim.

– Do you have any evidence of this?

– Nae exactly, Sir.

– I'm sure DCI Branning would've established a link if this were the case.

– DCI Brannin couldnae find his cock if it was located oan his forehead.

– At least I can find my way to the bath. You smell like shit.

Somethin snaps inside n ah launch at the fat fucker. He raises his hands tae defend himself, but he need nae have bothered – mah legs buckle beneath me n mah vision becomes a flickerin projector reel ay black n white.

Now aam oan mah back, lookin up at concerned faces all around me.

Ah fade out n fade up, hearin words.

– I never touched him.

Then everythin fades tae black.

Jack

Where am ah? Whitewashed walls. Disinfectant stink. A drip runnin intae mah arm. How did ah end up in hospital?

Memories flood back – the chest pain, mah body hittin the floor ay Brannin's office.

How pathetic. Ah put mah fist in mah mouth n bite hard.

Someone else is in the room – ah can sense them watchin me.

Chief Superintendent Morris sits in the corner with his arms folded. He's got a strange look oan his face – somethin between pity n simmerin rage.

– Welcome back to the Land of the Living, he says tae me.

– How long have ye been sat there?

He gets up from his seat n approaches the bed. – About two hours.

– Ah feel privileged. I would have thought a busy man like ye would've had better things tae dae.

– That's right, Jack – you try and make a joke out of this. When were you going to tell me?

Oh shit! Could he know about the cancer n the death sentence hangin over me? No, it wasnae possible. Doctors had tae abide by patient confidentiality – their word was their bond n nothin could break that. Ah decide tae style it out. There could be a number ay reasons why eh'd passed out.

– Tell you about what? ah ask.

– The cancer, Jack!

Fuckin useless blabbermouth doctors!

– That was private!

– Were you ever planning on telling me that you've got months to live?

– They had nae right.

– That's bollocks, Jack and you know it. You had an obligation to tell me. As your superior officer, I need to know if you have any problem which may interfere with your duties.

– Ah have nae problem carryin out mah duties.

– That's not how I see it. What if you'd been driving and you'd passed out like that? You could've killed someone.

– That wouldnae happen.

– You can't guarantee that.

– What are ye sayin?

– I'm sorry, but I have no option other than to pull you from active duty.

– Sir, ye cannae do that!

– I have to. When you're not collapsing, you're angry and irritable. You've shown no respect to your colleagues and worst of all, you keep shouting your head off about this serial killer without the slightest shred of evidence.

– There is a killer.

– Jesus, Jack – don't you ever give up? DCI Branning has assured me that these murders are isolated incidents and not connected.

– Wi all due respect, DCI Brannin is talkin out ay his arse.

– See what I mean, Jack? This isn't you. You're obviously under a huge amount of stress. You can't work like this.

– Please, Sir, ye have tae listen tae me.

– You need to stop this! We go a long way back. Are you trying to make my life difficult? You know what the tabloids are like – you say the words 'serial killer' and everyone goes nuts.

– Sae, what am ah supposed tae dae now?

– I don't know. Your doctor says there are things they can do for you. There are places you can go.

– Ye mean a hospice? Is that really how ye see me livin out mah last days?

– I don't have any answers, but I can't let you work in this condition.

There is a knock at the door. DI Nikki Cooper pops her head in. What the fuck is she daein here?

– I'm sorry, Sir, she says. – There's a call for you.

– Thank you, Nikki, I'll be along shortly, Morris says.

Nikki backs out ay the room, her eyes carryin sympathy. Oh Jesus, nae pity from her too – anythin but that.

– Does she know? ah ask.

– I don't think so, I certainly haven't told her. I haven't told anyone.

– Good! Ah want tae keep it that way.

– Don't you think your colleagues ought to know? Don't you owe them that?

– Ah dinnae owe them shit.

– Sorry you feel that way. Nikki certainly has genuine affection for you.

Mah mind flashes back tae the night Nikki made a pass at me. Ah can still smell her perfume in mah nostrils. What could have been if ah hadnae bottled it?

– I need to leave now, Morris says. – I'll arrange to have your caseload reassigned. You need to focus on feeling better.

– Don't ye remember – aam a dead man walkin? There is nae better – just varyin degrees ay worse from now oan.

– We'll do what we can for you, I promise. You're not alone.

– Funny, cos it feels like you're throwin me tae the wolves.

– We'll talk again soon, he says. Then he is gone.

Nikki comes back intae the room. – Are you ok? Do you want me to stay with you?

– Nae! ah say, closin mah eyes.

When ah open them back up, she's gone. Sae this is it – this is how ah end up – a bag ay bones waitin tae die. Ah think about the killer, wonderin what he's doin tae Anne-Marie Towers right now. Is she still alive? She needs me tae find her.

Now aam rippin the drip out ay mah arm, throwin oan mah clothes n chargin out the door.

CATFORD, SOUTH LONDON. 1984.

– What the fuck are you doin, Clayton, you little fuckin pussy?

He's been drinking again – he slurs his words and stinks like a gin factory.

– I'm peeling potatoes.

– Why you doin that, you little faggot? That's woman's work – you wanna be a woman – is that it? Maybe I should buy you a dress.

– Mum asked me to do it!

– Your mum is a fuckin ore, an you are a useless girly faggot!

I ignore him. I know he doesn't like that. He moves toward me. The booze stench makes me want to chuck.

– Did you not hear me, you deaf little cunt? Aren't you going to say sumfin clever?

I say nothing.

– I saw you hangin about with that little black boy again today, he continues. – Is he your boyfriend or sumfin? You wanna be careful hangin around them niggers.

He's looking for an excuse to whack me, so I give him one.

– You ever heard of a toothbrush? I say to him. – Or do you use dog shit for toothpaste?

I steady myself and wait for the punch or the kick, but it doesn't come.

He just smiles at me.

– You're turnin into real tough kid, ain't ya? he says, messing up my hair, before heading down the hallway, whistling to himself.

I let out a huge sigh. I'm not sure how I managed to get away with that. Maybe he's getting soft. I turn and start peeling again, thinking about the hair ruffle and how that might be the only affection that bastard has ever shown me. I crack a smile. That's when the alcohol stench hits me, and strong arms wrap around my chest.

– You fink you can talk to me like that, you little cunt? You fink you're a hard man, is that it? he says.

– Please, you're hurting me, I say, as he pushes my face into the kitchen worktop.

– You fink you're real fuckin clever, dunnt ya?

He stretches out my arm and rolls up my sleeve, exposing bare skin.

– You ain't that clever, he says. – You can't even peel skin properly. Your technique's all wrong. Here, let me show ya ow to do it.

– Noooooooooooo!

Clay

I peak out the window as the Black Beamer pulls up. Rain pounds the windscreen. What stupid spastic would be dumb enuff to drive in this shower of shit?

The old woman tries to shout a warnin, but Spivey has got his and over er gob. Not that it matters, the wind is so fuckin loud you couldn't ear a fog'orn.

An old man gets out the driver's side – looks like he's alone an must be fifty pushin sixty years old.

He ain't gonna be any kinda problem.

– What are you going to do? Danny asks, teeth chatterin from the cold.

– I'm gonna get me a car!

– He's an old man.

– An she's an old woman, I say, pointin to the old bitch. – But that don't change the fact that both a' them are gonna be dead in the next five seconds.

– Please, don't do this.

– Don't you ever get tired a' sayin that? I give Spivey the nod an he slits the old bitch's throat. Arterial spray shoots from the wound, hittin Danny full blast in the face.

The old girl drops to the floor, twitchin an jerkin – tongue lollin in er mouth like them stray dogs I used to torture on the estate when I woz a kid.

I take out my Beretta, flick the safety off an tuck it into the back a' my jeans, waitin for the knock at the door, but it dunnt come.

I look out the window. The old cunt has stopped alfway up the driveway with a dumb look on his face – lookin apprehensive, now backin away. He must've clocked our footprints in the mud or maybe he noticed the damaged door.

He calls out. – Margaret, are you in there? Is everything okay?

Fuck this! I've ad enuff of waitin for this senile old cunt.

I open up the front door an step onto the porch with a big welcomin smile on my face. I've always been complimented on my ability to get people trustin me. I don't know what it is – whether it's my bright blue eyes, or my handsome features, but people are drawn to me.

But not this geezer. He straightens when he sees me an steps sideways toward the car, so I whip out my Beretta an point it at im.

– Don't move! I say.

He freezes immediately – foughts tick through his head, but it ain't the blind panic you normally see when an old cunt gets a gun pointed in his face. Eyes flicker left an right, probably tryin to figure out the quickest way to cover. He looks back at the Beamer's open door.

– Don't do anythin stupid, I say. – Believe me, you'd never make it!

– Who are you? he asks, raisin his hands.

– Enuff with the questions.

– Where is Margaret? Is she okay?

– I said no more questions, dinnt I, arsehole? You wanna get shot in the face?

– I *want* to make sure she's ok.

– She's fine – she's in the kitchen makin trifle. Why dunnt you do yourself a favour an toss me your car keys?

The old man looks doubtful, but what choice does he have? He digs the keys out of his trouser pocket an tosses them to me.

– Are you a gamblin man? I ask im.

– Not really.

I old my dice between fumb an forefinger. – How about a game of chance?

– Do I have a choice?

– Of course, I could easily kill ya now, I say, aimin at his forehead.

– When you put it like that, I suppose I'd love to play a game.

– You seem strangely calm. Most people cry like a girl when they get a gun pulled on em.

– I used to be a commodities trader – any nerves I may have had were fried a long time ago.

– You were a banker? An I was just startin to like you!

– Sorry to disappoint. So, are you going to tell me the rules?

– The rules are simple; you roll a six an you walk away.

– And what about Margaret? Does she get a roll too?

– Who is that old bitch to you?

– She's my friend.

– I'm sorry, but the only rollin your friend is gonna be doin is when she goes in the grave.

He swallows ard an chokes on his words. – What do the other numbers mean?

– You dunnt wanna know!

– Looks like I'd better get myself a six then.

– I hate to break it to ya, but no one has ever rolled a six an I've been doin this a long time.

– A loaded dice?

– Nah, whatever you roll will be fair. You got my word on that.

– It's not easy to trust the word of someone pointing a gun at me.

– Fair game, I say, liftin the Beretta. – Now, you better get started.

He rolls an the dice lands in the mud. I can't believe my fuckin eyes.

The old geezer looks hesitant. – So, I guess you'll be letting me go on my way, he says, turnin.

– Yes, I say. – But there's just one thing!

I shoot im in the gut an he hits the deck like a sack a' shit.

Now he screams at me. – You gave me your word you'd let me go!

– An I will, but I can't just let you walk off to the nearest police station, can I? I've shot you in the abdomen, which is a really shitty fing to do, but you ain't gonna die – not if you're sensible an you crawl into the house, keep yourself warm an don't move. I'm sure the phone company will have the phone workin again in a few hours, so you'll be able to call yourself an ambulance. I'm really sorry about this.

– Screw you! he screams.

Yeah screw me, I fink to myself as I get behind the wheel of the BMW, startin up the ignition.

Danny climbs in alongside me while Benny an Spivey get in the back.

– Now let's go an find that little bitch, I say. – She can't a' gone far!

I look in the rearview mirror. The old man crawls away from the cottage. Where's he tryin to get to, I wonder? It don't really matter. He'll be dead soon.

Dumb cunt should've listened to me.

Joe

Once again, I buy flowers from the yellow-toothed crone and make my pilgrimage through the cemetery. I lay the flowers in front of the headstone and whisper.

– I miss you!

I hope you can hear me, Charlotte, but you're gone and you're never coming back. I'll never see your beautiful face again. That's what hurts most – the absence of you. You were like a supernova exploding into my shitty little universe.

And now you're gone. Your gorgeous body reduced to dust and bone. You only asked me to do one thing and I fucked that up, didn't I?

I can never make up for what I did. The shame will eat me up until the day I die. The Hunger won't let me forget. It's my penance – my punishment. The eternal reminder of all the terrible things I've done. And I will endure it – I would suffer the agony of ten thousand hells if it meant you'd forgive me. I'm so sorry, Charlotte.

I hear the crunch of gravel over my shoulder. – I thought I told you to wait outside, I say without looking back.

– My life is in mortal danger and you're leaving me stood around on street corners. What if someone followed us here? And don't give me any of that 'hiding in plain sight' crap, Becky replies.

– No one followed us.

– Yeah, and how do you know – are you some kind of super-spy or something?

– Something...

She stands by my side, looking down on Charlotte's headstone. Her dark hair blows in the wind.

– I'm sorry, she says after an uncomfortable silence. – I tried not to come, but deep down, I'm just a nosey bitch.

I laugh out loud. Her honesty is refreshing. Charlotte would've liked it too. It's a tragedy they would never meet.

An image of Charlotte's face flashes in my mind, and I think back to the last time I saw her – in that hospital bed when she'd gripped my arm and said those words just before she died.

Promise me, Joe!

– I'm sorry, Becky, I say.

– What are you sorry for?

– There are lots of things I never told you about me. I made money using girls like you. I've hurt people in ways you couldn't possibly imagine.

– But you've stopped all that now. You're helping me.

– I don't think one good deed can undo everything I've done. I wish it could, but redemption is way out of reach for me.

– Give it a rest, will you? Who do you think you are – some kind of anti-hero with a tragic backstory? You're not the only one who's made mistakes. You say Charlotte was special?

– She was.

– And she loved you?

– Yes.

– Then that's all that matters. I ain't had anyone love me, who didn't want to use me for a sponge. You don't how lucky you are.

– You haven't heard the worst of it. There's something else – something really bad.

– Worse than being a psychotic ex-gangster, who dresses in drag and talks to himself?

– Much worse.

Now she looks really worried.

– When Charlotte got pregnant, I was the happiest man in the world. We bought a house and I stopped working with Charlie. I actually believed we could be happy and then, six months into her pregnancy, Charlotte got these pains, and then she started bleeding. At the hospital, they told us the baby needed to be delivered immediately, but being so premature, there was little chance the baby would survive.

– Charlotte lost a lot of blood during the procedure and they couldn't stop the bleeding. It was like her whole body was shutting down. She knew she was dying, but the only thing she cared about was our little boy. I told her that he was in an incubator and was not expected to live much longer.

– She didn't look sad or scared about that – she just took my hand and told me our son was going to live because I was going to look after him. She made me promise to lavish so much love on that little boy, to give him a reason to stay in this world. At that moment, I would have promised her anything. I would've promised to move Heaven, Earth, and the stars in the sky if it'd lessen her pain.

– After she died, I went to visit my son. He was this pathetic, shrivelled thing. I couldn't see a baby no matter how hard I tried. I could only see the monster that took my wife from me. And then I had this horrible voice in my ear. *Are you going to let that little fucker live? He took everything from us.* So, do you know what I did?

Becky shakes her head – her eyes fearful of what I might say next.

– I left the hospital and went to a bar. I left my little boy all alone in that place. It must've taken half a bottle of whiskey for me to come to my senses: this was my baby boy – the last living part of the woman I loved. I had to be there for him, so I rushed back to the hospital but when I got there, the doctor told me that he had died half an hour after I'd left. I failed him and I failed Charlotte. I killed our son!

– You can't blame yourself, Joe. The kid was sick – sometimes people just die, and there's nothing you can do about that.

Her words do little to ease my guilt. Shame leaks like sweat.

– Now you know what I am, I say. – I'll understand if you decide not to stay. I'll give you whatever money I have, and you can disappear if that's what you want.

– That depends, she says with a devilish smile. – How much money are we talking about here?

I shrug. – A few hundred thousand, I guess.

Becky coughs in disbelief. – How much? What are you still doing here if you've got that kind of money lying around? We could get out of this shithole and go and live on an island somewhere.

– Charlotte had always talked about moving to the country.

– The country?

– Yeah, you know – that place with green fields that lies beyond the city.

– I know about the country, you sarky git! Well, I've seen pictures anyway. Now she's studying me intently, reading the sadness in my eyes.

– It really isn't your fault, she says. – Your son would've died no matter what, and if Charlotte was as special as you say, she'd forgive you. I'm sure she still loves you.

– She can't still love me because she's dead.

– So, you're not a big believer in Heaven then?

– No, are you?

– Of course! There's got to something better than this shithole, otherwise what's the point?

I wish I shared her faith. – Sorry, but when we die, that's it! Death is absolute – an absolute nothingness. One minute you're thinking about how bright the sun is, and the next second, you're not thinking at all. Death is an unfinished sentence!

– You're a real morbid guy – you know that?

I can't disagree with her. – I've even bought a plot for myself, I tell her, pointing to the patch of grass beside Charlotte's grave.

– You can't be serious?

– Yes, I thought I should be here with my wife – and also my son.

– Your son?

Now she looks at the small marble headstone stood to our left – the objectification of my eternal shame.

She reads the inscription out loud. – Here lies Thomas Quinnell, Beloved son.

Joe

Becky watches telly whilst demolishing a bowl of Sugar Puffs. She's got her hair tied into pigtails and wears the skimpiest pair of shorts I've ever seen.

I suspect she's trying to elicit some kind of reaction from me. If I look, I'm just another pervo and if I reprimand her, I'm a God-fearing Bible basher out to sermon her on the error of her ways.

Well fuck that – I'm not falling for that trap. I'll let her go her own way and hopefully, she'll grow to trust me and realise my motives are benign.

– *But are they, Joey? Are they really? Look at her. She's gorgeous, isn't she? Don't tell me you haven't noticed. She could easily pass for eighteen with her makeup on.*

Shut up! Get out of my head!

– *What's the matter – feeling guilty? It's not as if she doesn't know what she's doing. Look at those lips. I bet she knows her way around a cock.*

I pour a Whiskey – suitably large enough to drown the voice in my ear.

– *You faggot!*

Becky looks up at me. – Drinking again?

I flash a smile. – Looks like.

– Why don't you try and do something more constructive?

– What – like watching cartoons? I say, pointing to the cartoon cat who's being smashed over the head with an oversized wooden mallet.

– Maybe we could listen to some music. What kind of music do you like?

– I don't like music.

– I'm sure you do. We just need to find some songs you might like.

She gets up from the sofa and turns on the radio. We spend the whole afternoon listening to music. Some has me wishing I had access to hardcore narcotics, but others aren't too bad.

– Which one is this again? I ask, quietly admiring one tune but trying to maintain casual aloofness.

– Why? Becky asks excitedly. – Do you like this one? Her face is full of glee, and now I'm wishing I'd styled it out. I could live my whole life without knowing the name of this song, but I'm not sure I can cope with Becky's gloating. I don't know why it's so hard to admit that I might actually take pleasure from something. I've become used to playing a grumpy bastard – it's a role I've played for so long, I don't know how to be any other character.

Is this what life is like for normal people – you know those individuals whose lives aren't riddled with violence and horror – where you can sit indoors for hours in the company of someone you care about? Is this what it feels like to be happy? It's been so long, I can't remember.

– Can you make me one of those? Becky asks when she spots me pouring another drink.

– You're not old enough.

I get a roll of eyes.

– Cut the shit, Joe, I wasn't old enough to do a lot of things.

I look at her. She's so damned young and now I'm angry about all the shitty things she's had to do to survive – things no adult let alone a child should be forced to do. I pour a whiskey and hand it to her.

She looks surprised. – I didn't think you'd buckle so easily.

I shrug. – Like you say, it's probably too late to civilise you, and besides, you would only go and swig from that vodka bottle you've got hidden in your bedroom.

Her jaw drops open. – Have you been going through my stuff?

– I'm an alcoholic, Becky. I can smell that crap on your breath a mile away and I don't buy that piss, so you must have your own stash hidden somewhere. Your bedroom seems like the most logical place.

– You should be a detective.

– No, I'm not a big enough arsehole.

– You sure about that?

I don't respond. I just watch her grimace as she sips my very expensive whiskey.

– That good, eh?

– It tastes like my arse.

– Are you kidding me? You'll happily drink Russian piss, but you don't appreciate a bottle of Scotland's finest?

She looks down and examines the bottom of her glass. – I was thinking about what we was saying the other day in the graveyard.

– About what? I can't remember. I was pretty wasted.

– We was talking about moving to the country.

– Don't start that again.

– Why not?

– You know why not! You need to go to school!

– They have schools in the country, and they're probably better than the shithole you've got me going to. You should see some of the people they've got down there. I was eating my lunch with a knife and fork, and they was looking at me as though I'd just invented fire.

– I'm sure the kids aren't that bad.

– Who said anything about the kids? I'm talking about the teachers.

– I think you may be exaggerating. I must've told you a thousand times, do not exaggerate.

She plays imaginary drums. – Ba dum dum tush! Are you here all week? Cos I fucking hope not!

– I thought that was funny.

– You'd think Lenny Henry is funny.

– Who?

– It doesn't matter, anyway you're changing the subject.

– We are not moving to the country!

– What about my lungs?

– What about them – you're breathing just fine, aren't you?

– Do you know how many fumes there are in London?

– No, but I have a feeling you're going to tell me.

– You're basically killing me by keeping me here.

– Now you're being melodramatic.

– It happens to be true. It was on the news the other day. They said the air was full of these toxic fumes that cause cancer.

– Since when do you watch anything but cartoons?

– I'm telling you the truth. The police were talking about that house in the country again, you know the one where they found all those bodies. Apparently, they still haven't caught those evil bastards yet. After that, they had this guy talking about the stock market.

– The stock market? Now, I know you're bullshitting me!

– I can be highbrow you know.

– I'm sure you can.

– Don't patronise me.

– I wouldn't dare.

– I don't know why you're so dead against it. We could both do with a fresh start.

– What would we even do in the country?

– I don't know – raise sheep, churn butter – you know, the usual stuff country people get up to.

– Doesn't sound that great to me.

– And what's so great about what we're doing here? All I do is go to school or sit in this shitty flat, watching you drink yourself to death. You could easily drink yourself to death in the country.

An image pops into my head – me standing at the bar of some quaint country watering hole. I'm decked out in corduroy and it looks like Barbour has thrown up all over me. It isn't a sad image. Look – I've even got a smile on my face. And now I'm thinking about those scumbags out there looking for Becky.

Maybe she'd be safer out of the city.

– If I say I'll think about it, will you stop going on?

– Maybe, she says with a smile.

She's quiet for five minutes and then she starts nagging again.

Gabby

I've been silently stewing on my bed, marinating in my rage for thirty minutes. The same questions revolve around my head. How could Laura be so stupid? How could she consider having a child? Is she doing this to punish me?

I look out the window as lightning flashes. Trees sway in the wind.

Ben's car is gone. Where did he go in this weather? Off to visit Margaret, no doubt. Well, she can have him. The selfish bastard never backs me up anyway. Why does he care about her so much? Maybe he's got a thing for old grannies.

No – he's just one of those annoying do-gooders, who make you feel shit about yourself by showing you up to be a bitter and vengeful person.

There is a knock at the door. I open it up and find Laura standing there, holding a glass of red wine.

– Peace offering? she says.

– You're being foolish if you think you can get around me so easily.

– Okay, I'll just take this away then, she says, moving back toward the stairs.

– I didn't say I didn't want it, did I? I say, snatching the glass.

– Are you going to come back downstairs?

– I didn't think I was wanted.

– Ah, so you're still sulking then.

– I am not sulking!

She circles my face with her forefinger. – You see this? This is a great big sulk!

We sit on the bed and share an uncomfortable silence.

Laura speaks first. – You know, you should really learn to trust me. I'm not actively trying to piss you off.

– How come you're so good at doing it then?

– It's my life, I'll live it how I want.

– But a child, Laura?

– I'm not completely useless. I am capable of looking after a child.

– You say that now, but you'll change your mind when you're changing dirty nappies.

– I don't want to argue with you, Mum. Should I get an abortion? Would that make you happy?

– Of course, not! I just can't believe you've allowed yourself to get in this position.

– What position?

– Unemployed and pregnant at twenty-two.

– I'll be honest with you – none of this was planned, but now I can honestly say, I'm looking forward to the future. Unless you're saying, I'm going to be a shit mum?

– That's not what I'm saying, but I just hoped for something better for you.

– What – a nine to five job? That may have been your dream, but it's not mine. It's not the glamorous rock and roll lifestyle you think it is. You think you made a mistake staying in Greybrook, but you didn't! I look at what you and Dad have, and that's what I want.

– But why Josh? I blurt that out without thinking, immediately ticking myself off. Me and my big mouth.

– What's wrong with Josh? Why don't you like him?

– I just don't.

– That's not a reason.

– I can't tell you why I don't like him. It's the same with mushrooms, I don't know why I don't like them – I just don't.

- You're comparing my fiancé, the father of my child to a mushroom?

- That's not what I meant, and you know it. So, when do you think you'll get married?

Laura's response is cut short by frantic banging downstairs. Someone is at the front door.

Perhaps Ben lost his key. I peek out the window and look down on the still-empty parking space.

The pounding continues.

We rush downstairs as the door opens – Josh must've opened it.

A young girl screams. What the hell is going on?

In the hallway, Josh cradles a teenage girl in his arms. She wears a school uniform, which is soaked through. Her hair is drenched, matted down against bleached white skin. Teeth chatter behind purple lips.

- Pleeeeaaasseee, she says over and over.

- What's wrong? Josh asks her. – Have you been in an accident?

- Pleeeeaaaasssse....you've got to help me. They're coming for me.

- Who? Who's coming for you?

- Men... they kidnapped me. You've got to call the police.

- I'm a policeman. You're safe now. You don't need to be scared anymore.

The girl doesn't look convinced. She is terrified, and Josh's reassurance does nothing to curb her fear. Hairs stand on my neck.

- Please, you've got to get help. They're chasing me!

She's freaking me out now, so I reach for the phone and dial 999. No dial tone.

- Fuck! The phone's dead!

- It's the storm, Laura tells me, pulling out her mobile.

She needn't bother. She knows there's no mobile signal out here. How many sulks and arguments had we suffered when she was growing up, when she'd been the only one of her friends who'd been unable to use her mobile phone from home? How many times had she tried to convince us to move house for that very reason?

She looks up from her phone screen. – Nothing! Josh, do you have anything?

Josh shakes his head.

The girl looks even more panicked now. – Oh God! We've got to get out of here...they're coming for me. They'll find me.

Josh sandwiches her face in his hands and stares into her eyes, trying to hypnotise some calm into her. – You'll be safe here. They won't find you.

She grabs his arms with claw-like hands. Her eyes are wild and frenzied.

– We're not safe here! You haven't seen these men. They tried to rape me...he said he was going to kill me!

I've heard enough, and now I'm running to the back of the house, opening up the broom cupboard, feeding shells into Dad's old shotgun with shaky hands.

There is a crash from the hallway. A terrible scream follows. My heart pounds in my ears as I rush back to the hallway, where my worst nightmare unfolds in front of my eyes.

The schoolgirl is pinned up against the wall by a sadistic-looking freak who holds a knife to her throat. Josh kneels on the floor with his hands on his head – blood runs from a cut above his eye. Then I see Laura struggling in the arms of the scariest looking man I could have imagined – a demon dressed in a man's skin.

He holds a gun to her temple. She looks so scared.

I aim the shotgun at his face. – You take your hands off her, you fucking prick!

– Don't be silly, darlin! You an me both know that if you fire that fing, you'll not only hit me, but you'll also make a real mess of this pretty girl's face. Now you dunnt wanna do that, do ya?

I know he's telling the truth, but I try and keep a poker face. – You let her go, and then you can get the fuck out of my house!

– That ain't gonna appen, he says. – But I promise you: if you don't lower that shotgun in the next five seconds, I'm gonna redecorate your walls with brain, an please know, I ain't jokin.

I believe him. This man is capable of complete evil. He looks insane. He would have no problem killing Laura. He would have no problem killing any of us, but what can I do? If I lower the gun, I give up our only leverage. – You hurt my daughter, and I'll blow your fucking balls off!

That draws a laugh from him.

– That really don't bovva me, darlin! Me an Death ave walked side by side for quite a while now.

With a deft movement, he turns the gun from Laura's head, so it's pointing at me.

– Now for the last time, he says. – Lower that fuckin gun before I do sumfin you regret.

I look at Josh and hope for guidance, but he looks lost. He's never been in this situation before – he's never been out of control. All his arrogance and swagger has evaporated and now a frightened boy is left behind. My mind spins. A thousand scenarios run through my head, and none of them end well. The only thing I know for sure is that Laura will die if I don't give up the gun.

Tears run down my face as the shotgun clatters to the floor.

– Well done, the demon says to me, smiling. – You just saved your daughter's life.

Yes possibly, I think to myself. But for how long?

Joe

I'm sat in the Three Bells, and I'm absolutely shitfaced, having worked my way through a bottle of twelve-year-old Macallan.

– I hope you're planning on payin for that, Fred – the obese and disgustingly unkempt landlord says to me.

– Just put it on my tab.

He raises a greasy eyebrow. – You ain't got a tab. In fact, I don't even know what you're doing here seeing as I barred you last Thursday.

– What for?

– You was in here, wearing a dress and makin a right old racket – ended up causin a fight. Put two geezers in the hospital. You don't remember that?

– No, sorry, you must be thinking of someone else.

– There can't be two people as irritating as you!

– There's a whole army of us.

– Don't say that, you'll have me up all night wetting the mattress.

– Don't lay that shit on me – incontinence is normal for someone your age.

Fred glares at me with fiery eyeballs. – One of these days, I'm gonna smack you right on the nose!

– Just bring me another bottle, Rocky Balboa.

– You ain't paid for the other two yet.

I take a roll of notes from my pocket and toss it at him. – Pick it out of that, I say.

He shoots me a disapproving look, before returning with another unopened bottle. Something occurs to me.

– Two? What do you mean 'two'? I've only had one bottle.

– No, you've had two.

– Don't fuck me about.

– I ain't fucking you about. You've had two bottles, so I'm chargin you for two bottles.

– I can't have drunk two. I'd be off my chops.

– You are off your chops!

– Yeah, but two bottles in two hours? I'd be in hospital.

– Lucky then that you've had two bottles in four hours, isn't it?

I point to my watch. – What are you talking about? It's 2 PM. I came in here at 12.

– No, it's 4 PM, he says, pointing to the clock on the wall. Hands point at twelve and four.

4 PM. Fuck! I was supposed to meet Becky outside the school gates at 3.15. She'll do her fucking nut. I almost fall over when I get to my feet, knocking over my bar stool, dropping my glass.

The fresh air hits me like a punch, and it takes a few moments to figure the way home. I stumble and swerve down the street, careful not to clatter into parked cars and camera–happy tourists.

I mutter whiskey–fumed apologies. Somewhere in the distance police sirens wail. At the corner of Frith Street, I'm knocked to the ground by some dickhead in a raincoat. He doesn't even apologise.

– Fucking wanker! I shout, but he's halfway down the street before I slur out the words.

Five minutes later and I'm home, heading up the stairs and unlocking the front door so I can retrieve the keys for the Mini. I notice the tiny scratch on the Yale lock but notice too late.

– Fuck! I say before there is a loud crack, and now, I'm on the floor, wondering what the fuck I'm doing here. I put my hand to my face – something sticky runs down my forehead into my eye.

Someone speaks to me in a deep Eastern European accent. – Stay down fuckface, or I'll give you another taste of this!

I rub enough blood from my eye, so I can see the biggest man in the world standing over me, wielding a baseball bat.

Fuck, I must be drunk if this vat of dripping can get the drop on me.

I try and scramble to my knees, but the vat of dripping is true to his word and whacks me again – this time in the sternum. Something breaks inside. Fuck, that hurts so much! I think I might cry.

Now there's a different voice in my ear – a softer Russian accent.

– He did warn you to stay down, didn't he?

A shaven-headed man peers down at me through horn-rimmed glasses. Two other men stand either side of him. The one to the right must weigh close to twenty-five stone and is built like a Rhino. The other one looks like he hasn't washed his face in living memory – his cheeks are pockmarked and covered with angry acne.

That makes four in total. All of them wear made to measure suits. Every inch of unclothed skin is covered in Russian gang tattoos.

– Do you know who I am? The shaven-headed man asks me.

– Well, you're not Jon Bon Jovi that's for sure – he's good looking.

– Oh, so you're a comedian. That's good. You're going to need that sense of humour. My name is Semyon Ivankov. I work for Nikolai Novichkov. Does that name mean anything to you?

– Sure does, wasn't he the winner of the gay pride awards?

– Stanislav, please teach the comedian some manners!

The vat of dripping hits me twice in the side with the baseball bat. I say bye-bye to a couple of ribs. Fuck it, collateral damage – got to keep these cunts talking until I regain the use of my legs – that hit to the head has scrambled my brain.

– Why are you doing this to me? I ask.

– Don't play dumb. You think I'm stupid…is that it?

– Well, you certainly aren't the smartest knife in the drawer.

That buys me two more digs from Stan's bat. My body feels like it's on fire.

Semyon removes his glasses and polishes the lenses. – Do you think we can stop playing these silly games now?

– You're missing the scar, I tell him.

– What?

– You need a duelling scar on the cheek if you're going to complete the look. You've got the stupid glasses, the bald head, but you need the scar if you're going to go full Bond villain on me. And don't forget the fluffy cat – the cat's essential.

– Do you think you impress me? You think you look tough talking this way. You don't look tough. You look stupid. You took Nikolai Novichkov's money – now a price must be paid.

– I don't know what you're talking about.

– Of course, you don't – but you might want to start knowing, because things will get real bad for you if you don't start talking. Where is the money?

– I told you, you've got the wrong guy.

– It's amazing how many times we hear this thing. We always have the wrong guy, then when we start removing teeth, it turns out we have the right guy – it is uncanny. Why don't you tell me what I want to know before we make a mess?

– How can I tell you what I don't know?

– I'm getting bored now. Mr. Novichkov says we have to make an example of you, but he says we can go easy if you give up the money. You will suffer very badly, I'm not going to lie about that. I doubt you'll ever walk again, and you'll probably piss blood for a year, but at least you'll remember your name. If you keep up this amnesia act, then we're going to leave you as a…. sorry, I don't know the word in English…an ovoshchnoy.

– A vegetable, I mutter through gritted teeth. My ribs hurt so much.

– You speak Russian? Where did you learn to speak Russian?

– In another life, I tell him.

– Now we know the money isn't in the flat because we checked already – so where is it?

– *Well well well this doesn't look very good, does it?*

Where the fuck have you been?

– *I thought I wasn't wanted. You've spent the best part of the day drinking yourself to death like some pathetic loser. Why would I want to stick around and watch that? I disappear for a couple of hours and look what shit you've landed us into. I suppose you want me to bail you out of this fuckfest too?*

That would be helpful.

– *Maybe I don't want to. Maybe I'll just sit back and watch you get a good pasting. God knows you deserve one!*

If I get a pasting, you get a pasting. Do you want us to end up as a dribbling vegetable?

– *Better than watching you poison yourself with that manky Scotch piss! How long do you think your poor liver can hold out? Better spastic than dead – for me anyway. I suppose it might suck for you a bit.*

Help me – please!

– *Sorry, I can't hear you. Now the question is: what kind of vegetable would Joe be? A potato? A parsnip? How about a carrot?*

I suppose if they rupture your spleen and crush your liver, you'll end up going a little bit orange like a carrot.

Help me!

– *Beg me!*

What?

– *You heard! Beg me or else!*

Okay, I'm begging you!

I must've said that out loud because Semyon's laughing at me.

– Begging won't help, he says.

He's looking really menacing now. I don't have long until he's commanding Stan to hit me with that bat again.

– *Tell me that I'm the best and that you need me!*

I need you and you are most definitely the best! Happy now?

– *Ecstatic. So how are we going to deal with these fuckers?*

Not being funny, but I thought that was your job?

– *Do I always have to point out the bleeding obvious – when exactly did you become so fucking useless?*

So, you've got a plan then? Don't keep it to yourself.

– *The ugly one – inside jacket pocket.*

Ugly one? – could you be more specific?

– *Okay, the really ugly one.*

I assume you're talking about the poor sod with the pockmarked face.

– *See the bulge under his leather jacket. You know what that is, don't you?*

Ruger – P90.

– *You need to get hold of that gun.*

But my legs are fucked. I can't move.

– *Your legs are fine. Stop being a moaning pussy. I'll tell you exactly what you're going to do.*

I thought you were going to handle this?

– *How come I always have to do the heavy lifting? No, I think I'll just sit back and watch this time. Now here's what you're going to do.*

The voice whispers detailed instructions in my ear.

– *Now did you get all that?*

You can't be serious? They'll pick me off as soon as I move.

– *Not if they don't expect it. Make them think you're weak when you're powerful.*

Before I know what's happening, I'm sobbing like a little girl. – Please don't hurt me, I say over and over.

They laugh at me.

– We heard you were tough, Stan says. – What a disappointment, I was looking forward to breaking you.

Heads roll with laughter.

Suddenly, I'm on my feet, charging at Scarface, driving the palm of my hand into his nose. I reach into his jacket, pull the Ruger from its holster, and fire two shots into his heart, before spinning around and aiming at Stan who swings his baseball bat, knocking the gun from my hand. He's about to swing again when I step in close, put my thumbs through his eyes and bite off his nose.

Semyon reaches for something behind his back, so I spit blood and cartilage into his eyes to buy myself time.

The twenty-five stone rhino charges at me. I catch him with a vicious uppercut. Teeth fly in the air, eyes roll back, but his momentum sends him into me and now I'm on my back with the tub of lard on top of me. I try and push him off, but Semyon stands above me, aiming a Glock at my face.

– I mocked you, Mr. Myers, he says. – For that, I eternally apologise, but now it is time to say goodbye.

He cocks the gun.

– I thought you wanted to know where the money was.

– The money was never important. The message was all that mattered. You are not right, Mr. Myers. The world will be a better place without you. It would be wrong to let you live. Are you ready?

I close my eyes.

The gunshot echoes in my ears.

Something's wrong. My brain should be splattered across my living room floor, incapable of firing electrical impulses of sound to my ears.

I open my eyes and look up at Semyon, who examines a hole in his stomach, wondering how it got there.

Becky stands at the front door, holding Scarface's smoking Ruger. She looks comical in her school uniform – I'd laugh if my ribs weren't ready to pierce skin.

– Drop the gun, she says. – And back up or the next one goes through your face!

Semyon must believe her because he does as he's told without protest.

– Can you move? she says to me.

– Yes, I say, pushing the rhino off me. Suddenly I can breathe again, which isn't good because breathing really hurts!

– Don't be silly, little girl, Semyon says. – Do you know who I work for? He's a dangerous man. Not someone you want to piss off.

– Call me 'Little Girl' again, and I'll turn you into one, she says, pointing the gun at his crotch.

I try and get to my feet but collapse immediately. The adrenalin has worn off. My body is a roadmap of pain. Becky bends down and helps me, keeping the gun trained on Semyon. She leads me outside, opens the door of the red Mini, and lays me across the back seat.

– What are you doing? I ask when she sits behind the wheel.

– Saving your arse by the look of it. Oh, and you're welcome by the way.

– You haven't got a license!

– Well duh, I'm only fifteen years old.

– You'll get us killed.

– Looks like you've been trying to do that all by yourself. Do you want to drive?

I try and sit up but my body screams.

– Okay, now that's settled, she says. – I suppose we can get going.

– Oh, fuck!

– What is it?

– The keys are in the flat.

– Don't worry, she says, fiddling under the steering wheel.

The ignition starts up.

– When did you learn to do that?

– Do you really want to have that discussion now?

We pull away from the curb as sirens approach. Neighbours must've called the cops when they heard the gunshot.

– Have you ever driven a car before? I ask her.

– I might've stolen one or two.

– And did you ever crash?

– Only the one time.

Jack

The blast throws me through the air. Time slows.

Ah hang for an eternity until ah hit the floor. Pain rips through mah side n smoke fills mah lungs. Ah examine mah left hand. Three fingers are bent at freakish angles. Dad's voice echoes in mah head – That's gonna sting in the mornin, boy!

The world spins – reality has skewed n nothin makes sense. When the smoke clears, the screamin starts – a soul suckin shriek chills me.

Ah stagger tae mah feet, shakin like a lump ay jelly as ah move toward that awful sound.

A car alarm blares. Bodies lie strewn across the road. Blood pools on the cobbled streets. Ah see the charred remnants ay a child's doll – there's always a fuckin child's doll at a disaster scene, isn't there?

That's when ah see him or what's left ay him.

Private Dean Blakely lies oan the pavement. The bottom half ay his body is gone, mutated intae a twisted mess ay muscle n testicles. His neck muscles bulge as he tries tae sit up – thankfully, he can only raise his head two inches off the ground, sae he's unable tae see the damage.

 His eyes widen when he sees me. – Sarge! Sarge! I can't feel my legs, he says.

Ah drop tae a knee by his side. – Don't move. Try n stay still. Everythin'll be okay.

– I can't move my legs.

– Yer legs are fine.

Guilt washes over me, but what else can ah say? Your legs are blown tae shit n sae are yer balls.

– You promise, Sarge?

– Ah promise.

– Thank fuck for that. I thought I'd copped a bad one for a minute there. Megan would've been pissed. The wedding's only three weeks away.

– Try nae tae worry. Everythin's goin tae be alrite. You're gonna make the wedding – don't ye worry about that.

 – But I can't move my legs.

Sirens approach. Hurry the fuck up! Everythin around me is chaos, but ah have tae keep it together for him.

– Ah promise yer legs are fine – you're just stunned.

– Are you sure? They feel funny...please tell me...you're lying, aren't you?

Ah try tae reassure him but choke oan the words.

– Oh God, my legs are gone, aren't they? Please tell me, I need to know.

– You'll be fine.

– Stop lying to me! My legs are gone. I know they are. Please, this can't be happening – no, it's just a dream – a really bad dream. I just need to wake up. Oh God, why won't I wake up?

– Listen tae me! Ye need tae calm down.

– Don't tell me to calm down! This is your fault!

– What? Dinnae say that – please! Ah couldnae have known.

– You knew! You did this! You were in charge!

– Please....

Ah cradle his head n somethin spongy touches mah fingers. His eyes roll back. – Stay wi me Dean, stay wi me!

Somethin comes free when ah move mah hand from his head. Ah open mah mouth tae scream, but nae sound comes.

Ah jerk upright n scream the nightmare away. Mah body is covered in sweat n the sheets are soakin wet.

In the bathroom, ah splash cold water on mah face n check mah reflection – eyes are tiny pinholes, swallowed by black rings.

What has the cancer done tae me? Ah dinnae recognise the person lookin back.

Ah switch off the bathroom light, head tae the kitchen n grab a beer from the fridge. Mah eyes settle oan the framed photo oan the wall. Ah trace mah finger over Mary's face. Here ah am again – the walking cliché – the sad, pathetic detective drownin his sorrow, lamentin the loss ay his family.

Ah sit on the sofa. A fan-like display ay gruesome images stare back at me from the coffee table – dead girl's faces locked in eternal contortions ay fear n pain.

Who did this tae ye, girls? Please help me. Ah might have let mah own daughters down, but ah willnae let ye down. Aam goin tae catch this monster for what he's done.

I head over to the chest ay drawers in the far corner of the room, take out the wooden box within, n bring it back to the sofa.

Inside, there are photos ay mah time in Northern Ireland. Eh'd looked sae strong n healthy back then. There's a photo ay Dean Blakely wi his arm around me – we're both smilin.

The nightmare had been inaccurate. He never blamed me for what happened tae him n he would nae have done if he had lived. He was too good a friend for that, but that dinnae stop me blamin myself.

Ah should've looked out for him.

Ah remove everythin from the box until only one item remains – mah old Brownin service revolver.

It feels heavy.

Has it really been sae long, or has the cancer eaten away mah strength? Ah look back oan the faces ay the dead. How long will it be before Anne-Marie Towers joins them? A've got tae find her.

Mah finger twitches against the Brownin's trigger.

– Don't worry, mah old friend, it willnae be long now, ah promise!

Laura

Me, Mum, Josh, and the schoolgirl are on our knees in the living room with our hands tied behind our backs. The psycho creep paces up and down, asking our names. We tell him, and then he introduces himself and his vile companions. He's almost civil – polite even. You wouldn't think he'd smashed his way into our house, taken us prisoner, and held a gun to our heads.

The schoolgirl is crying her eyes out. I'm doing my best not to do the same. I've watched reality crime TV shows where they say it's best to keep calm in situations like this, but every part of me wants to scream. I keep thinking back to those train journeys into London, when I'd wished to be anywhere else. Now I would do anything to be back in that office, with The Big Swinging Dick – I could suffer that fate for all eternity if it would transport us from the grasp of this sadist.

Clay stops pacing and looks down at the schoolgirl. I have a bad feeling. He lifts her chin with his forefinger. – You can't even look at me, can you, Kirsty?

She sobs loudly. A bubble of snot erupts from her nostril.

– Please, she says, over and over. The word comes out in soul-wrenching sobs, barely discernible as words.

– Sssshhhh, he says, silencing her with a finger across her lips. – Save your pathetic dribblin for someone who gives a shit. You lied to me, Kirsty. You said you was gonna be a good friend to my bruvva, but you proved to be the worst. Do you remember what I said would happen if you fucked with me?

He takes a dice from his pocket and tosses it on the floor. It rolls across the carpet until it hits Spivey's foot.

– So, what have we got, Corporal? Clay asks him.

– Looks like we've got ourselves a four.

– Outstandin! Clay says, drawing a knife from behind his back.

Kirsty cries more loudly now. – Pleease....pleease...

– Don't cry, Spivey tells her. – Believe me, it could've been much worse.

– You should believe im, Clay says. – So, you wanna know what appens now? I'm gonna take this knife an slit your throat. You might fink that ain't too bad, but that's because you've been watchin too many movies. See, when you slit someone's throat, they don't just drop-down dead like you see in the films. It takes a good minute or so to die, an durin that time, you'll be squirmin around, pissin blood from your throat. If you got any last words, you might wanna say em now, cos you ain't gonna be sayin nothin with a severed windpipe.

Kirsty starts blubbing. I want to find the words to stop this, but a coward has possession of my body. I want to scream for this madness to stop. The words freeze in my throat. And then the words I want to say are being said out loud, but they're not coming from me.

– Leave her alone, Josh says. – She's just a child.

That makes Clay smile.

– Why do you do-gooders always say annoying things like that? He reminds me of you, he says, turning to Danny who shuffles nervously. He's not like the others in the group. He does not want to be here.

Clay grabs Kirsty by the hair and pulls her to her feet. She screams when the knife touches her throat.

Josh leaps to his feet, barring his teeth like a Rottweiler. – I said, leave her alone you piece of shit!

I've never seen him like this. He looks like a different person. He is still screaming when Spivey pulls him back to the floor.

– Look who woke up, Clay says. – You've been sat there lookin like you're gonna shit your pants an now you wanna be an ero. Spivey, cut his restraints!

Josh looks confused.

– I tell you what we're gonna do, Clay says. – Me an you are gonna fight. If I win, the girl bleeds and bleeds bad. If you win, then all four a'ya get to walk out a' ere.

– Am I supposed to believe you'll just let us go?

– I give you my word!

– And how do I know you'll keep it?

– I always keep my word, boy. You'd do well to remember that!

– What about the knife?

Clay lays down his knife.

– And the gun?

The gun follows.

Josh still looks doubtful and I don't blame him. This guy oozes evil. – Okay, he says, as Spivey cuts his wrist ties.

– Josh – no! I say, blood thudding through my ears. Mum shoots me an imploring look – stop him! But what choice do I have? What choice does Josh have? Anyway, Josh is a talented boxer. He'd enjoyed a successful amateur career and had toyed with going pro when he was eighteen but had been talked out of it by his mum, who feared he might become punch drunk or have his looks spoiled. He'd trained his whole life for a moment like this. But that was training. This was for real.

Josh gets to his feet. Fear is written all over his face. I've never seen him look so vulnerable – so frightened. I want to throw my arms around him – to tell him that everything will be all right, but I've never felt more helpless. All I can do is give him a look: you can do this!

– Come on then! Clay says, beckoning Josh forward with arms outstretched, chin up in the air.

Josh springs into action and unleashes a flurry of punches. I am amazed by the speed of the assault. It's hard to believe this is the same man who spends ninety percent of his time slobbing on the sofa, who refuses to do washing up as though fearful his hand might disintegrate should it come into contact with soapy water.

Clay is also shocked by the speed of the attack, barely avoiding a punch aimed at his jaw. He is not so lucky with the next strike, which connects with his nose. Blood spurts from his nostrils. Confidence surges through Josh. He's so much quicker than his opponent – his movements more powerful and ferocious.

There is a loud crack as Josh hits Clay on the cheek. The larger man looks unsteady, the wounds of battle are evident on his face.

My body fills with hope.

But why do I have this bad feeling? And why are Clay's associates looking so pleased with themselves? Spivey smiles wickedly and the retard giggles inanely. Now I notice a gradual but noticeable change in Clay's movements. Where he'd been clumsy and tripping over his feet, he was now nimble as a cat – easily ducking blows that had been hurting him moments ago.

Spivey's smile grows as Clay easily avoids another punch. And now a horrifying realisation hits me. The bastard is toying with Josh and now Josh is starting to notice. His shoulders drop. Frustration and panic fill him. He grabs Clay's arm and attempts to throw the larger man over his shoulder, but he does not move – he holds his feet and pulls Josh close.

– Looks like you've done some training, he says. – But this ain't no boxing match!

There is a sickening crack as Josh's arm snaps with a movement so fast, I don't see it.

Josh stares disbelievingly at the shattered appendage for an agonising moment before the screams start.

Clay lifts him and slams him into the dining table.

– What else have you got, ero?

Clay is laughing now – the sound is like daggers stabbing my ears.

Josh struggles to his feet, arm hanging limply by his side, blood dripping from where fractured bone has pierced skin.

– I've got to admit, I'm impressed, Clay says. – You've got eart kid but eart ain't enough. There ain't a man alive who can take me in a fight.

Josh roars and lunges at him, but the attack is clumsy and easily dodged. Clay kicks at his knee, buckling the joint.

Josh tries to crawl, but he can barely move. His body is broken in so many places.

– Where are you goin, boy? Don't you wanna fight no more? An you were doin so well!

Clay grabs Josh's ankle and twists until it snaps. There is another scream. I never thought a human being was capable of making such a sound. I would do anything to untie my hands so I can cover my ears.

– Now let's play a little game of Piggy! Clay says, locking an arm in his grasp.

He breaks the little finger first.

Then the wedding finger.

I can't believe this is happening. Josh barely looks like the same person anymore. His face is twisted red with agony.

The middle finger breaks.

A scream escapes my lungs.

– Please stop! Please leave him alone.

Clay smiles. – You want this to end?

– Yes, I say, the words are strangled with salty tears.

– You're sure?

– Yes!

– You're sure, you're sure?

– Yes, please stop hurting him.

– Okay, but I want you to remember – you asked for this!

And then he does the most terrible thing. He twists Josh's head so hard, bone crunches and muscle tears. Then something breaks inside. I scream, praying this is some horrible nightmare.

What does Dorothy say?

If I click my heels three times... There's no place like home, there's no place like home. But I am home and this place is Hell. I collapse on my side, hyperventilating, barely able to breathe.

– Looks like I won, Clay says, standing over me.

And then Kirsty's face lands on the carpet in front of my eyes. She squirms and chokes, blood pumping from a gash in her throat.

Laura's lesson for the day – it sure takes a long time for someone to die from a slit throat.

It sure isn't like the movies.

Joe

The balding hotel manager glares at me from behind the reception desk. – What's the matter with him? Is he drunk?

– No, he's just been released from hospital, Becky says, keeping me upright with an arm around my waist. – He was in an accident.

– Really? What happened? Did he walk into a whiskey factory? He stinks!

– A car hit me, I tell him.

Although technically a lie, it doesn't feel far from the truth. I'm pretty sure my busted ribs are dangerously close to puncturing a lung with a jagged edge.

– You two look like trouble. You're not gonna give me any shit, are you?

Becky gives him a butter wouldn't melt look. – We're just looking for a room, so my dad can recover before we head home to Manchester.

– And how long do you want the room for?

– A week – maybe longer.

The hotel manager raises an eyebrow. – A week, you say? You got cash to pay in advance?

– How much is it?

– Three hundred quid.

I almost cough up a lung, and my side goes into spasm. – Three hundred quid to stay in this shithole?

– Three hundred pounds is fine, Becky says, pinching my side.

I take out my wallet and remove two hundred in twenties.

– You're short! he says.

– I'll pay the rest once I've had a chance to get to a cash point. I hadn't pre-planned for anal rape today.

The hotel manager ignores me and takes a room key off the rack. – Number thirty-four, the best room in London.

– I doubt that, Becky says, shepherding me toward the stairs.

Every step hurts more than the last. I don't know what's worse – the pain in my side or that I can plausibly pass for Becky's father.

We get into the room, and my heart sinks. The walls are nicotine-stained, the mattress looks as though someone has died on it, and the cadaver has lain undiscovered for two years.

Becky pushes me onto the bed and removes my shoes.

– Why do we have to stay here? I say, sinking into the mattress. Bedsprings dig into my back.

– Where else would you suggest? The Savoy or The Ritz maybe?

– It's hard to imagine the sheets in the Ritz being starched with semen. This place is a shithole.

– People in shitholes know to mind their own business.

– People in the Savoy know how to mind their own business too. Rich people can get away with anything. I thought you would've worked that out by now.

– Stop complaining, will you? It's just a week.

– A week in Hell can seem like a lifetime – believe me!

– I see your injuries haven't stopped your mouth from working.

– A shotgun blast couldn't stop my mouth from working.

– I believe you. Now give me your wallet.

– Why?

– We need supplies. Maybe if I get you some painkillers, you'll stop moaning. I grab her wrist.

– You can't go out there. They'll be looking for you.

– You need medicine and you need bandages.

– I didn't have you pegged for a nurse.

– What can I say? I'm full of surprises.

– I'm serious, Becky, it isn't safe.

– We can't live off fresh air. We also need food and clothes. If you think I'm spending the next week wearing this school uniform, you've got another thing coming.

– Then I'll go.

Becky pushes me back down on the bed. – Don't be ridiculous, you can barely stand.

– I'll leap into action any second now. Just let me get my head around the idea of moving.

– You don't need to worry about me. I know how to stay hidden.

– Not in that outfit. You look like a right lemon. I should go. I'm supposed to be looking after you.

– That's all you've been doing since we met. You're always looking after me. Now it's my turn. She leans over and kisses my forehead. – I won't be long.

– There's something else I need, I say to her.

– What?

– Alcohol.

She bites her lip. – You don't need that.

– I do or The Hunger will find me again.

– *But I've already found you. I'll never leave you...you know that.*

– If it does, then we'll tackle it together.

– You don't know what it's capable of.

– But I know you. If it's part of you then it can't be all bad.

– I wish that were true.

– So, what'll it be? Jim Beam...Jack Daniels...

– Anything. If it's wet, I'll drink it.

She rifles through my wallet. – So, where's your bank card?

– I don't have one.

– What? You are joking?

– Nope. I don't even have a bank account.

– How are we gonna get money then?

– I told you, I've got money stashed away.

– Where is it?

– *Don't you fucking answer that little bitch. You tell her where that money is, and we'll never see her again!*

I tell her where the money is.

– Okay, you leave it with me, she says.

– You be careful.

– Always.

And then she is gone. Leaving me alone with the pain and The Hunger.

– *That's the last you'll see of her!*

Go fuck yourself.

– *Ditto.*

I wonder if I'll be able to sleep. There's surely no way, I think to myself.

Next thing I know, I'm opening up my eyes and Becky is sat beside me on the bed. She's already changed into a pair of jeans and a white t-shirt.

– How long have I been asleep?

– A couple of hours.

– Did you get the money?

– Sure did, she says, pointing to the sports bag at the end of the bed.

Shows what you know fuckface!

– *Blow me!*

– Would you like something to eat? Becky asks. – I got sandwiches. You can have cheese and pickle or ham and mustard.

– Later, I say. – Where's the liquor?

She hands me a bottle of Jack Daniels. – I got painkillers too.

– Give them to me!

– They're really strong. The guy said you shouldn't take them with alcohol.

– I don't give a shit – give em over now!

She hands me the packet, which bears a prescription label in the name of Ursula Van Helden.

– Where did you get these?

– Ask no questions and I'll tell no lies.

I rip open the foil packet and pop pills like they're penny sweets, washing them down with glugs of JD.

– I don't think you're supposed to take that many.

– I don't care if they fucking kill me. Death would be an improvement on what I'm feeling now.

– You shouldn't say things like that.

– Please tell me you got bandages.

She nods.

I teach her how to wrap my ribs tightly.

– When did you learn to do this? she asks.

– In a previous life, I tell her.

She pulls the bandage tight, and I yell in pain. I reach for the painkillers.

Becky grabs my hand. – I don't think you should take anymore.

– Who are you – my mother?

I pop three more.

– Look what I've got! she says proudly, brandishing a large hardback book.

I read the title out loud. – England's Most Beautiful Villages.

She lies down next to me, tucking my head under her arm. I feel like a sick child being read a bedtime story by his mum.

– I thought we should do some research, she says.

– Research?

– Yeah you know, try and find somewhere we'd like to move to.

Becky flips through pages.

– You're serious about this, aren't you?

– Yeah sure – aren't you? I bet this place Minster Lovell doesn't have any Russian gangsters trying to shoot you in the head. Look at this church – it's so cutesy.

– We're going to settle in Minster Lovell – is that what you're saying to me?

– Hold your horses! We've got a lot more research to do before we settle on a location. You just go to sleep and leave it with me.

I watch as she turns the pages, pointing out the ones she thinks I'll like – basically every single one with a pub.

– You could definitely get drunk here, she tells me, pointing to the Espen Arms in Little Brampton.

I'm feeling drowsy now. The drugs are kicking in hard. Everything is nice and calm. The sound of turning pages soothes. I haven't felt this close to anyone for so long. Not since Charlotte.

Eyes are heavy. They close. And then I am plunged into darkness. I hear screams and see faces long forgotten. And then I feel shame. I see Toby's face, but it isn't the face of the shrunken baby I abandoned all those years ago. He must be five or six now – standing there, clutching a teddy bear and sucking his thumb. Now Charlotte is here, wrapping her arms around me.

– Am I dead? I ask her.

She smiles and fades into blackness. Where did you go? And now I see Becky's face above me. She caresses my body, running soft fingers toward my crotch. Her body is pressed against mine. She kisses me on the lips.

How I've missed this – the warm touch of intimacy. I kiss her back, and the shame hits. What am I doing? She's only a child. I can't do this, or I won't be any better than the dirty old bastards who paid for her. I'll be no better than the Webrichs.

I'll be no better than any of them.

Don't be so hard on yourself. This is just a dream – a dark, subconscious fantasy. No harm can come from this. But why do I feel so dirty? I push her away and suddenly I'm so cold.

Her eyes look up at me from the black, so tainted with hurt and humiliation.

How could you do this to me?

And now the darkness closes in, and I think to myself, don't worry, this is just a dream.

No harm can possibly come from a dream.

Gabby

Laura and I are handcuffed to the radiator in the living room. I'm worried about her. She hasn't said a single word since....since Josh. What do you expect? She just watched her fiancé get beaten to death – what should she be doing – singing and dancing with joy?

– Laura, please speak to me.

She says nothing. Her face is pale – eyes red-rimmed and sore. A solitary tear forms a snail trail down her cheek.

– We need to find a way out of here, I say.

If she hears, it doesn't show. She doesn't even blink.

– I'm sorry about Josh but we need to get out of here before he comes back.

No response.

She remains silent – staring at the wall. My God, she's gone catatonic. What if she never snaps out of this? What if she never comes back to me? Stop panicking. She's in shock. Wouldn't you be the same if that'd happened to Ben?

Oh, my sweet Ben! Where the hell is he? Hopefully, he'd seen these bastards break into the house and driven straight to the police station. It's possible but not likely. Chances are, he's still at Margaret's. No doubt, the old hag has guilt-tripped him into a candlelit game of chess. Wherever he is, I hope he's far from this house.

But what if he isn't? What if he's on his way back here? What if he's driving up the hill at this very moment, unaware of the horror waiting for him? He was a retired banker and these men are killers. What chance would he have? Less than none.

– Laura, please talk to me! We need to find your father and get out of here. Can you hear me? Please say something.

Still nothing. More space staring.

Then she makes a noise – a mumble or a whisper.

– Did you say something?

– You never liked him! she says.

– What?

– You never liked Josh. You didn't want us to be together. Are you happy now?

– Of course, not! How could you even ask that? What Josh did was very brave, but we don't have time to grieve right now. We've got to escape.

– There is no escape. Not for us.

– You can't talk like that. You can't give up. Think about your baby.

– The baby you don't want me to keep, you mean?

– Please don't, Laura. We need to work together if we're going to get out of this.

– We're not getting out of this. We're already dead. Dad's probably dead too.

– No, Dad's fine, and we are going to get out of here! Do you hear me?

The living room door opens, and Clay enters.

– So, what are you two talkin about? You wouldn't be plottin to escape, would you?

– What if we are? I say. – Are we supposed to just sit here and wait for you to kill us?

He squats down and looks me in the eye. – Who says I'm gonna kill you?

– We've seen your faces. We can identify you.

– You do make a compellin argument. Aren't you frightened?

– You'd like that, wouldn't you? But you won't get that satisfaction from me.

The words come from my mouth but my body shakes. I hope he doesn't notice, but a man like this can probably taste fear.

Clay stands and walks the perimeter of the room, studying the photos on the wall and above the fireplace.

– I think I know why you're not scared. Perhaps you're opin to be rescued.

I try and keep my voice steady. – Rescued by who?

– I don't know, he replies. – Maybe by someone I don't know about.

He runs his finger along the wall, knocking a painting to the floor.

– Maybe someone who lives in this house.

He looks at the photo of four-year-old Laura on her first day at school.

– A lover maybe? But more likely...

He settles on our group family photo.

– A father...

He's got the photo in his hand now.

I squeeze my eyes closed.

– and a usband.

I open my eyes and my stomach sinks when I see he's pointing directly at Ben's face.

– And who is this andsome devil? he asks with a gloating smile on his face.

– That's my husband.

– And where is this usband now?

– Probably at the police station.

– Is that right?

– Yes, he left when Kirsty turned up.

– He drove, did he?

– Of course.

– Let me see if I can guess what car he owns. He looks quite sensible, so maybe a Citroen or a Skoda – no I've got it: a BMW, he says with a click of his fingers.

A fist grips my heart and squeezes.

– How do you know that?

– Cos, I ad the pleasure of meetin your husband.

Tears build behind my eyes, but I don't let them out. I won't give this bastard the satisfaction.

– I met im an our ago at this cute little cottage down the road.

– You're lying.

– You know I ain't. You wanna know what I done to your usband? You want me to tell you? I shot im in the gut an left im out there in the rain. Don't worry though – he ain't dead. Not yet, anyway. Thing is, it takes a long time to die from a gunshot to the stomach. That's the good news, but the bad news is, it urts a lot. You can't walk or barely even move. You just roll around in your own blood an filth – writhin in agony. He probly wishes he was dead. He'll be like that for hours, that's if he ain't bled out.

– I hope you fucking die slowly, you evil bastard!

Clay holds up his hands in mock surrender. – You shouldn't blame me, Gabs. I wanted im to live. If he'd listened to me, an stayed in that old bitch's cottage, he would've been okay, but he had other ideas. He decided to go his own way – I wondered at the time, where he was crawlin off to. I guess now I know. You should take comfort in the knowledge that he sacrificed imself tryin to get back to you.

– Fuck you!

– I hope you're this tough when you an your daughter face my dice.

– You leave her alone! You don't even look at her. You hear me?

– That sounds like an order.

– You're fucking right it is.

– You ain't in a position to order nobody.

– You touch her, and I swear to God, I'll fucking kill you.

– You'll swear to who? You really fink God is with you? You're sat in a house where you don't get no mobile phone reception, and a storm has knocked out your landline. Then four bad men break into your house. What are the chances a' that? It's like some sadistic author has written you into this shitty situation.

– No one's sadistic enough to do that.

– You should save your strength, Gabs an dream of appier times.

He drops our family photograph to the floor and swaggers from the room, singing Dreams by the Everly Brothers.

I look at Laura, hoping for some sign of life, but she's still slumped motionless against the radiator.

Rain pounds like pellets against the windows. I think about Ben lying out in the rain.

Shivering. Cold. Afraid.

The courage evaporates from my body, and I break down. It all feels so hopeless.

Now I feel Laura stroking my head.

– I think it's time we got out of these handcuffs and killed these fuckers, she says.

Jack

Ah wonder how many times ah will get tae walk through Soho like this? Will they miss me when aam gone? When aam nothin more than a feeble collection ay brittle bones, burst tumours sealed in a tight envelope ay skin. Ay course they willnae. These streets are tough n unforgivin – there's nae place for sentiment here.

Ah find Vicky oan Greek Street. She'd been one ay Snakeskin Eddie's girls, before he'd gone n done his disappearin act. A blue Citroen pulls up n she leans intae the open passenger side window. The driver clocks me n speeds off with Vicky's head still in the vehicle. She's pulled along for a few steps before managing tae extract herself, landin oan her arse.

She screams after the speedin car. – You stupid motherfucker! You could've taken my head off! Then she turns around, glarin at me. – You just cost me twenty-five quid, you Skeletor – lookin cunt!

– Hello, Vicky.

– It's Lucy, dickhead!

Aam genuinely mortified. A've always prided mahself oan knowin each ay these girls. Now aam wonderin who Vicky is. Oh, fuck it, it doesnae matter. Ah pull out mah wallet n offer her thirty quid.

– It's only twenty-five for a fuck, she says.

– You lookin for somethin harder?

– No, aam reimbursin you for loss ay business.

– You fink that's gonna cover the pain in my arse. I'll probably have a bruise now!

I give her another score.

– So, you wanna fuck or not?

– Nae, aam a police officer.

She lets out a snort. – That don't stop most of you.

Can't say aam shocked. I suspect plenty ay coppers take advantage ay these girls.

– Anyway, I eard you wasn't a copper no more.

Bloody hell, word sure gets around quick.

– Where did ye hear that?

She shrugs. – I dunnt know. You just ear fings sumtimes, dunnt ya? So, what ya doin – crawlin in your spare time, like?

– Aam nae crawlin.

– If you say so. So, what's the matter with ya? You're ill, right? You got AIDS?

– No.

– I have.

– What?

– Got the AIDs, well HIV anyway. Had the test two weeks ago. Come back positive – just my luck! It was all them injections Eddie gave me when he was getting me hooked on the Heroin. I suppose I weren't worth the cost'a clean needles.

– Aam sorry.

– Don't be, looks like I'll live longer than you anyway.

– Ah think ye might be right about that. If ah ever find Eddie, I'll make a point ay breakin his kneecaps for ye.

– Somebody already beat ya to it!

– What do ye mean? Eddie's still missin.

– You mean you ain't eard? Fuckin pigs – you ain't worth a squirt of piss, are ya? They found him in Epping Forest. Somebody fucked him up, and when I say fucked him up, I mean they fucked him up proper bad.

– Is he dead?

– Nah he's alive, but they dinnt leave much of im from what I eard.

Ah can barely contain mah excitement. This could be the breakthrough a've been waitin for. Eddie was the last person tae see Bella Hopkins alive. Maybe he could tell me what happened the night Bella went missin.

– Sae, where is he?

– Some hospital in North London.

– Do you know which one?

– St. Mary's, I think – um yes, that's the one.

Ah thank her n charge toward Leicester Square tube with a renewed sense ay purpose. Aam getting closer tae catchin this bastard, ah can sense it. Now ah see blue sirens flashin up ahead. A police cordon has been set up. A media crowd is gathered. The flare ay cameras blinds me.

– What happened here? I ask a wet behind the ears PC.

– They found another dead pro!

– How old is she?

The lad looks like he's about to throw up. – I don't know, but she's young. The bastard sliced her face to bits and he.... he cut out her tongue.

Joe

I dream a lovely dream. Most people don't know they're dreaming, but I do, because good things only happen in my dreams. They're tantalizing glimpses of what my life could be like if I didn't fuck it up at every turn. They give me things normal people take for granted – a house, a wife, kids. And then they're cruelly snatched away when I wake. Right now, I'm sat in a cozy village pub with a fire roaring at my side. A golden Labrador rests at my feet.

Becky is here too, but she's older now – she's turned into a beautiful young woman. She chats with local farmers at the bar. All the pain and anger has been washed away. She looks so happy.

She turns and gives me that same look.

You're so uncool.

Now her face changes as though she's seen something terrible over my shoulder.

I turn but nothing is there. Now she runs toward me, mouthing something, but I can't hear the words. She looks so scared. I remember her face – how it'd been filled with hurt and humiliation when I had pushed her away.

I open my eyes, and I am in darkness. My throat is dry. Bed sheets stick like glue. I peel them from my clammy body and shakily stand.

Am I awake or am I still dreaming? Now I remember where I am – back in the room of the fleabag hotel.

There is no sign of Becky, so I head to the bathroom and put my ear to the door.

Can't hear anything.

I try the handle and it opens.

Empty.

My throat feels like I've swallowed barbed wire, so I drink from the bathroom tap. It tastes like rust and fluoride. How long have I been asleep? It feels like months. My stomach roars like a lion.

I find a Mars bar on the side and gobble it down, barely taking time to remove the wrapper.

Flicking on the bedroom light, I immediately know something is wrong.

Becky's gear has gone. All the clothes she bought are missing. The book – England's Most Beautiful Villages rests on the side. Two words are written on the cover in biro.

I'm sorry.

Sorry – what is she sorry for? And then I remember her naked body pushed up against me. I remember the kiss and me pushing her away. I remember how she'd looked at me. Oh, fuck! What have I done? My heart pounds. I open up the sports bag on the bed – she hasn't taken a penny of the money.

You, silly girl! You should've taken me for everything I had. When will you learn if you don't take care of yourself, then no one else will?

What the fuck are you doing, Joe? You've got to get out of this shithole and find her. Those Webrich creeps are still out there – she's in danger. But where would she go? Back to Soho? Back to Charlie? Surely, she isn't that stupid. Of course, she is – she's young and tough – not a good combination when making sensible decisions about personal safety. She'd back herself to handle most situations. She might not fully understand the danger she's in.

I throw my clothes on quick as I can, ignoring the pain from my shattered ribs and head downstairs where the balding hotel manager sits behind the reception desk.

He looks up from his newspaper. – Oh, it's the Return of the Living Dead, he says. – At least you can walk in a straight line now.

I resist the urge to put his face through the reception desk. – I'm looking for my daughter, have you seen her?

He smiles at me. – Your daughter? You still peddling that bullshit, you dirty bugger?

– You know you should really go and see a dentist if you want a full dental extraction. Now I'll ask again – you seen her or not?

– Yeah, I saw her a couple of nights ago – looked like she was in a hurry.

– A couple of nights? What day is it?

– You serious?

– I'm fucking serious! What day is it?

– It's Wednesday.

Wednesday! We checked in late Monday afternoon. I've lost two days. How is that even possible? What were those painkillers Becky gave me?

– Did she say where she was going? I ask.

– She didn't say anything – she just walked out.

– What time was this?

– I don't know – about 11 PM.

I charge out of the door without another word. Becky's got a two–day head start on me. Where could she go? She'd need money, so Soho was a good place to start looking.

The thought of her working again makes me feel sick. I don't know what I'd do if I found her with a punter. Who am I kidding? I'd rip his cock off and shove it up his arse. I'd break his legs and smash him into a million pieces, and no one would be able to stop me.

I make my way to Charlie's office and find him behind his desk. The spider sitting in the middle of its web.

– Where is she?

– Well, hello to you too.

– Cut the shit, Charlie. You tell me where she is, and this can go quickly and painlessly.

– Cool your boots, Rambo. I don't even know who you're talking about.

– Becky!

– I haven't seen that little bitch since Darla's.

– And what about your little friends? Those Webrich faggots. They been looking for her?

– I told you to forget about those guys.

– If anything happens to Becky, I'm going to…

– Whoa! You don't need your threats – I haven't seen your little girlfriend.

– Okay, if you see her, you let me know.

I spend the next four hours walking around Soho, visiting every brothel, flophouse, and street corner. I speak to working girls, pimps, down and outs, but no one has seen Becky.

If anything happens to her, it'll be my fault. I let her down. I should've known something like this would happen. Everyone she's ever met has taken advantage of her, so why would she believe that she'd finally met someone who actually cared for her, who didn't want something in return? Maybe I'm underestimating her. Maybe she won't come back here.

She could've gone anywhere – Manchester or Liverpool perhaps – Northern cities have their fair share of sexual deviants who'd be willing to pay for a girl like Becky.

I'm close to Dean Street when I see the lights. I push past the crowd and see the body lying on the pavement, covered by a white sheet, surrounded by torn big bags and strewn rubbish.

Oh God no! Please don't let it be! I need to know if it's Becky. I know the odds are against it, but I have this terrible feeling in my gut. I duck beneath the police cordon and run toward the body.

A uniformed officer grabs me. I snap his forearm without thinking.

He screams.

I kneel next to the body and lift the sheet, exposing naked white flesh, tinged by pink neon lights. I see the cut where the knife has cleaved her face in two.

I scream Becky's name.

A hole opens in my stomach, and I want to fill it with all the pain and suffering in the world.

Another police constable runs toward me.

– Get away from the body, he commands.

The dumb bastard swings at me, but I've beaten him unconscious before he knows what's happening. Two police cars pull up, with lights flashing. Every part of me wants to tear them apart. I need an outlet for the raging hunger ripping through me.

– *Kill them! Kill them all,* the voice says to me.

I want to be with Becky. I want to take care of her.

But it's too late, I can't help her now. I failed her.

Four uniformed police officers sprint toward me – one of them is built like a brick shithouse. I make a run for it, and they chase me through the Soho streets, but they don't know this place like I do. They don't know the little nooks and crannies, where someone can disappear.

I lose them in the backstreets, before doubling back to the crime scene, climbing the fire escape of Dirty Ken's sex shop, and taking up a vantage point on the roof. More police have arrived – swarming like flies. The policemen I injured are being loaded into ambulances, and now I feel guilty for hurting them.

– *Don't be silly. That's what you do, isn't it – hurting people?*

I think about Becky's face and how it'd been sliced apart. Why did they do that to her? I'll hurt them for that – hurt them worse than any cunt has ever been hurt before.

A detective stands over her body – he looks like a paedophile in that raincoat. Having a good stare, are you fuckface? Get your dirty eyes off her and cover her up for fuck's sake. He looks up in my direction, so I slip back into the shadows. Did he see me?

No, doesn't look like it.

I stay for two hours until I've seen enough, then I descend the metal steps and hail a black cab on the street below.

– Where to? The cabbie asks.

– Curzon Street, and make it fast!

Jack

– How is he daein, Doctor?

– Pretty well considering he's suffered the worst injuries I've ever seen.

Ah try n hide mah revulsion as the Doctor tells me how Snakeskin Eddie's attacker had cut out both his eyes n chopped off his fingers. He'd also been castrated, and his tongue split down the middle.

The attacker has a sense ay humour, ah think tae mahself.

– Can ah speak tae him?

– We managed to sew his tongue back together so he should be able to talk. To be honest, I'm surprised it's taken you so long.

– What do ye mean?

– Well, Mr. Markowitz has been here for a few days now. I thought you would've been here sooner.

– Ye mean nae other police officers have interviewed him?

– There was another Detective who came when he was first admitted, but he didn't spend much time with him. I assumed someone else would be coming to follow up.

– But nae one did?

– Not until now – no.

– This Detective, do ye remember his name?

– DCI Maddison, I think.

Ah huvnae heard ay him, but there isn't anythin unusual about that. The Met is a big place, but ah can't shake the feelin somethin stinks here.

– Can ye tell me anythin else that might help me find who did this tae Sna....Mr. Marcowitz?

– Only that they weren't an amateur.

– Ye think they had medical expertise?

– I'm not a forensic pathologist, but those injuries should've killed him. Whoever did this was well versed in the art of inflicting pain without causing death.

Thirty seconds later, aam sat at Snakeskin Eddie's bedside. He's got white patches over his eyes.

– It's DI Travis, Eddie – do ye remember me?

– Of course, I remember you. You tried to fit me up for dealing Heroin.

– Ye were guilty.

– Bullshit! I was innocent, and you tried to fit me up.

– An argument for another time. Why don't ye tell me how ye ended up in that bed? He says nothin. – If you're havin difficulty, let me get ye started. Ye were seen gettin intae a car with Bella Hopkins. Two days later she was found floatin in the Thames without a head. Yer turn.

– I'd been supplying young girls for these VIP parties at this house in Knightsbridge. I was makin more money than I'd ever seen. Everything was going well, but then things started to change.

– Change how?

– The girls would go, but then, they didn't come back.

– Sae, what did ye do?

– I went to the house and kicked off. Some fuckin ape opened the door. I asked him where my girls were. Thought he was gonna break me in two at first. Then he told me to fuck off and wait for a call. When I got back to my flat, there was a package on my doorstep with twenty-five grand inside. Then I got the call – some posh prick told me that if I kept the girls coming, the payments would keep coming too.

– What about the girls? What happened tae them? Did ye ever think tae ask, or did ye not care?

– I didn't want to know, the money was too good.

– Sae, what went wrong?

– I got greedy. After I dropped the girls off, I'd sit and watch all these rich pricks turn up in their sports cars and their limousines. They had so much money. I realised they could afford so much more. They were playing me for a fuckin fool!

– Did that make ye angry?

– I thought I could get more out of them. You know – like millions. So, the next night, I took a video camera with me.

– Ye were plannin tae blackmail them?

– Yes, I went to the house to make my drop, but the guy at the door told me they urgently needed another girl. Apparently, some little bitch had skipped out on em earlier that night. I said I could get another girl for them.

– Bella?

He nods. – That's right, but they asked me to deliver her somewhere else.

– Where?

– Out in the middle of nowhere. Some place called Ashenridge. There was this building – a huge church with black walls – it was the scariest place I've ever seen. I dropped off Bella, but I didn't leave – I parked the car and looked for a way to get inside. The whole place was locked up tight as a drum, but I found this broken basement window, so I snuck in, and I saw... His voice breaks, his body shaking uncontrollably.

– What is it, Eddie?

– What I saw....My God, what I saw....

– What was it – what did ye see?

– I can't tell you. You'll have to go and see for yourself. They must've known I was watching – known I was there, cos they were waiting for me when I got outside.

– Who was waitin?

– These men in red gowns. I ran, but they caught me and then he did this to me.

– He? Who is 'he' Eddie?

– The Devil.

– Ah dinnae believe in the Devil.

– If you'd seen the things I'd seen, then you'd believe. Maybe that's why he took my eyes.

– Why leave ye alive?

– Have you seen what he did to me? It was crueller to leave me like this. I can't even kill myself, he says, holdin up bandaged, fingerless hands.

– What about the tape, Eddie? What happened tae the tape?

– They took it from me.

– And DCI Maddison, tell me about him.

– He told me they'd caught the man who did this to me, so they were closing my case.

– Really?

– Yeah, but it was bollocks – he was tryin to cover it up! I'm not even sure he was a cop.

Ah stand n smooth mahself down. – Goodbye, Eddie, eh'd like tae say it's been a pleasure, but that'd be a lie.

– Wait! You can't leave me like this. What's goin to happen to me now?

Ah stop at the door n look back at the pathetic lump ay flesh. – Are ye serious, Eddie? Ye corrupted dozens ay young girls n got them hooked oan Heroin. Ye literally drove children tae their deaths, sae you'll forgive me if ah don't shed any tears for ye.

Ah leave him wi his pitiful sobs n a've never been prouder with mahself.

Joe

The black cab pulls up outside the mansion in Curzon Street.

I hand the cabbie a twenty and tell him to keep the change. I look up at the wrought iron fence and the security cameras. I remember thinking it would be impossible to sneak into the house unseen, but I don't give a fuck about that now. I scale the wall in one movement and stride toward the front door. I ring the doorbell and wait.

The Tattooed Penis, Phil who'd first approached Becky at Darla's, opens the door. He looks at me confused, probably wondering how I managed to get past the gate.

– What the fuck are you doing h...

I put my thumbs through his eyes and snap his neck before he can scream.

I move into the house and sneak down a hallway lined with portraits of aristocratic arseholes in tweed. The smell of mahogany and polished surfaces in my nostrils.

I kill two security guards quickly and silently before moving upstairs via a winding marble stairway.

Snooker balls crash in a room up ahead on the right. I find the super-tough SAS man, Rudd inside, leaning over a billiard table with a snooker cue in his hands.

He looks up at me and smiles – the same smug smile he gave me at Darla's. – I was hoping you'd show up sometime, he says.

I charge toward him. He swings the cue at my head. He's quicker than most, but not quick enough. I duck down and kick at his knee, buckling the joint, so his leg forms a right angle with the floor. I hit him in the throat with the V of my thumb and forefinger, crushing his larynx, strangling a scream in his throat. Then I grab his head, forcing it down into his neck until vertebrae snap and pop.

With a stamp on his head, I finish the job and leave the Billiard room, continuing down the corridor, following the distorted screams of a young girl.

The sound is horrific – it's coming from behind that red door at the end of the corridor.

What the hell is happening to her? I haven't heard screams like this since...

I push the door open. Augustine Webrich leans back in a leather chair with his feet up on a desk. He's gripped by something on a television screen – that's where the screams come from.

I creep toward him silently.

He sees me out the corner of his eye, almost tips over before managing to right himself, reaching into his desk drawer. I am onto him in a flash, slamming the drawer shut on his hand, shattering bone. He lets out a scream, which I enjoy, so I slam the drawer again.

More bones break. He sobs and piss runs down his trouser leg.

– Please stop!

– Is that what she said? I say, pointing to the jerky image on the television screen.

A teenage blonde lies across a stone altar. Her body is covered with blood, her eyes wide with horror. A man wearing a priest's cassock and a red cape stands over her. A mask obscures his face. Then I see the surgical scissors in his hand.

– You sick bastard, I say to Augustine, slamming the drawer again.

– Do you know who I am? he says. – I click my fingers, and you're a fucking dead man!

– I'd better make sure you don't click your fingers then, hadn't I?

I place his other hand in the drawer, slamming it repeatedly until ring and index fingers have been sliced off.

Blood pumps from ragged stumps.

He shrieks in agony. –What do you want?

– I want to hurt you. I want to hurt you for what you did to Becky.

– It wasn't me!

– Don't you lie to me!

– It wasn't. I swear to God.

– God can't help you!

I jam my thumbnail into the soft flesh behind his right eyeball, pushing against the nerves.

Augustine lets out another scream. – It wasn't me!

– So, who was it? Was it your girlfriend in the red dress? Who is that faggot, and where do I find him?

– You have to promise to let me go.

I start laughing. – Are you that fucking stupid? You're already dead, you just don't know it yet! You've just got one choice left to make: you can die quick, or you can die slow!

He sobs like a child, so I jam my thumb behind his eye again until the eyeball partially slides from its socket.

– I'm never gonna get bored of hurting you, so you better tell me what I want to know before I rescind my offer to kill you quickly.

– Okay, he says, pointing to the wall with a bloody hand. – That's where you'll find him.

I look up at the painting, realising that I've seen this building before. I saw it in George's book, The Silent Snake: A Horrible History of the Webrich family. I'm looking at the monastery in Ashenridge.

– Thank you, Augustine. Shall we get started?

– Started?

– Yes, I'm going to hurt you. I'm going to hurt you worse than you can imagine.

– You said you'd kill me quickly.

– I was lying! I say. – And when I'm finished with you, I'm going to find your little bum chum in the red dress, and I'm going to do the same to him.

Augustine laughs – the kind of laugh that stands hairs on end. The laugh of a madman. – You have no idea what you're walking into, do you? He'll see you coming from a mile off.

– He's just a man, and he's going to beg just like you.

– He is no man! He's not even human.

Augustine keeps laughing. The sound makes me angry. He only stops when I start removing his face.

Laura

– It's no use, Mum says, as she massages the handcuff chaffing on her wrist.

– Don't give up, I say.

– It won't work, I tell you!

– Keep your voice down, or that freak will be back in here!

For the past ten minutes, we've been pulling at the handcuffs, hoping that they or the radiator pipe would give way.

Neither has budged. It doesn't help that we have to work in absolute silence, otherwise, we'd be discovered.

– We have to think of something else, Mum says.

– Like what – asking him to let us go?

– I could ask to go to the toilet.

– Then what?

– Once he's unlocked the cuffs, we attack him.

– With what?

Mum's eyes settle on the family photo Clay had dropped. – We could break the glass and use it as a weapon.

– Are you serious? You want to engage that psycho in hand–to–hand combat. You saw what happened to Josh?

– He won't be expecting it. He thinks he's broken us. We can catch him off guard.

– He won't go for it. He'll probably get off watching us piss ourselves.

– We have to do something. If we sit and wait, they will kill us eventually. It's miraculous he hasn't done it already.

– I know that.

– So, what other options do we have?

– I don't know – I'm thinking.

– Well, don't think too long. Hold on – someone's coming.

The living room door opens. Clay and Spivey walk in.

– Looks like the rain has stopped, Clay says. – Which means, we'll be leaving soon. I'm sure you're both sorry to hear that. Mum and I say nothing, but we don't disguise our hatred for this bastard.

– You really hate me, don't you? Clay says, with a laugh.

– You're a monster, Mum says.

– You fink you're better than me, dunnt ya? Wot just cos you live in this big fuckin ouse, in this shitty little village? You ain't no better than me. Life is a game a' chance an you been the lucky ones – until now. I used to be lucky too, but my luck changed one day when a waitress served the wrong table. Now, we're gonna find out if your luck is gonna old out.

He opens his hand and shows us the dice. My heart pounds. I think about how Kirsty had looked with her throat sliced open.

Clay sees my fear. It draws a perverse grin. – Are you ready, Laura? Let's see if you're as lucky as your dad.

– You leave her alone! Mum screams at him. – You can kill me, but you leave her alone!

– Don't worry, Gabs, he says. – Your turn will come, but I fought you'd wanna watch your daughter go out first. You can kiss the dice for good luck if you want!

Mum spits in his face. – Fuck you, you sick fuck!

– A simple 'no' would've sufficed, he says, wiping saliva away with his hand, sucking it from his fingers. – Let's get started, Laura.

– What does each number mean? I ask him.

– It's probably best that you don't know, but let's just say, ya wanna avoid one to five.

I close my eyes, trying to force images of Kirsty from my mind. It doesn't work – I picture her twitching on the floor, frantically clawing at her neck wound. Will that be me in a few moments?

The dice hits the floor. I pray for a six.

When I open my eyes, Clay is smiling at me. He looks so happy it breaks my flesh into goosebumps.

– Spivey, go an find us some shovels, he says.

Jack

Ah ring the doorbell n wait.

Nae answer. I'd expected as much from the empty driveway. Ah think about postin the envelope in mah hand, when ah hear a voice behind me.

– Hello, Jack! Is that you?

Ah turn around. – The one n only! How are you, Gwendolyn?

– I'm well, Jack. We haven't seen much of you around here.

– Eh've been busy.

– Are you here to see Mary?

– Aye, have ye seen her?

– She told me they were going to the zoo for the day. I'm not sure what time they'll be back.

Ah stare at the envelope in mah hands. – Can ah ask ye a favour, Gwendolyn?

– Of course.

– Can ye give this letter tae Mary for me?

– Sure, I'll give it to her as soon as I see her.

– Nae! Do ye think ye could give it tae her oan Monday?

– Okay....

– Please, Gwendolyn, it's important that she doesnae see this until Monday.

– Okay, Jack, but what is this all about?

Some things ne'er change! The Earth spins, the world goes round n Gwendolyn is still a nosey neighbour.

– Ah just need tae know she'll get this.

– I'll give it to her on Monday – I promise.

– Thank you, Gwendolyn.

I cross the road n open up the door ay mah Renault.

– Is everything okay, Jack?

– Aye, everythin is fine, ah say before drivin off, followin directions to Ashenridge.

That nosey bitch had better nae open that letter.

Jack

Ah park up behind a crop ay trees sae mah Renault willnae be seen.

If there had been any life in Ashenridge, it was dead now. Mah torch beam cuts through the night as ah walk through the deserted village.

It doesnae take long tae find the old monastery Snakeskin Eddie had told me about – the spire pokes out above the tree line ay the wood up ahead.

Ah tread carefully through thick vegetation, duckin under low branches. Soggy leaves squelch underfoot. Now ah can see the buildin clearly n it looks like somethin from a nightmare.

The walls are charcoal black wi sharp pinnacles stabbin the sky. It is surrounded oan all sides by a graveyard littered wi weathered headstones, covered in moss.

It doesnae look like anyone has been here for a long time. Aam startin tae wonder if Eddie has played me for a cunt. Then a light goes on in a top floor window. A silhouetted figure stands with its face n hands pressed against the glass.

Ah duck down. Is it lookin at me? Nae – that isnae possible, unless they can see in the dark. After a few agonisin moments, it moves away. The light goes out.

Ah do a reccie ay the buildin, movin around the circumference. Most entry points are sealed up tight, but ah manage tae find the broken basement window Eddie had told me about. Ah check mah watch – four o' clock in the mornin.

Sergeant Cole, who'd been mah drill instructor in the paras sounds off in mah head.

You don't know the layout of the building, so you need to wait for daylight.

Aam startin tae shiver. Mah teeth chatter. Ah need somewhere tae hole up until the sun comes up. How about that small buildin annexed tae the right-hand side ay the monastery? Yes, that'll do.

Ah get down oan mah hands n knees, crawlin through the graveyard.

Keep your head down, Private unless you want to feel my boot!

Ah find a hole in the wall n squeeze through, cursin out loud when mah elbow scrapes exposed brick.

Stop being such a mincing faggot! I seen worse injuries the last time I tugged too hard when I was looking at a picture of your mother!

Ah switch oan mah torch, shinin the beam around the room. Dust particles hang in the air. Oh fuck, aam goin tae sneeze.

Don't do it, arsehole, you'll give away our position!

Ah pinch mah nose n hold it. Then ah sneeze one ay those ridiculously loud sneezes that would make everyone in a packed room jump like an idiot.

The sound echoes through the chamber like a broken record. Ah switch off my torch n wait in the darkness, listenin for sounds stirrin in the night.

Blood thuds in mah ears.

Ah wait five minutes n hear nothin. Satisfied, ah click the torch back oan, lightin up skulls piled high tae the ceiling. Oh, mah God! How many girls has this sick fucker killed?

Ah pick up a skull n examine it. Jack, you're a fuckin idiot. This isnae a young prostitute's skull – if it was, it wasnae one who died recently. This is an old skull – possibly centuries old. This buildin must be the charnel house that serviced the original monastery. These must be the bones dug up from the graveyard when they needed tae make room for fresh corpses.

Sittin in the corner, ah take mah place amongst the dead. There's still two hours n forty-five minutes until sunrise. Ah close mah eyes n see Anne-Marie Towers. What if she's being tortured right this second n aam sittin here cowerin in a corner? What if she needs me now?

Ah remove the Brownin from its holster, flickin off the safety. Then aam crawlin back intae the night, headin toward the monastery – toward the open basement window.

What the fuck are you doing, you stupid prick? You're going to get yourself killed! You should wait until sunrise.

Ye taught me sae many things, Sergeant Cole – how tae crawl through muddy trenches, while avoidin barbed wire. Ye taught me how tae yomp, carryin a twenty-kilo backpack, but ye never taught me how tae wait.

Jack

Ah drop down from the basement window n land oan a stone floor. It is pitch black, sae ah flick oan mah torch n shine it around.

Aam standin oan some kind ay viewin balcony, lookin down oan a large rectangular chamber with an altar at its centre. Dried blood covers its surface.

Ah spin around, sensin someone watchin me from the shadows.

Nae one is there.

Scaredy cat. Scaredy cat.

Tae mah right, there's a heavy wooden door. Ouch! What the fu...ah pull my hand away from the metal ring handle, examinin a cut in mah hand – a three-inch gash pissin blood. How did that even happen? Jesus, there's a metal spike stickin from the wood.

Ah wrap mah hand with a handkerchief, then try again, carefully twistin the metal ring this time. The door opens, revealin a stone staircase leadin up.

At the top ay the stairs, ah emerge intae a hallway wi regal red carpets n oak-panelled walls, lit up by ornamental lamps. The monastery interior has been gutted n completely refurbished. It feels like aam walkin around a stately home.

Puttin mah ear tae the nearest door, ah listen for sound. Nothin, sae ah turn the handle n step inside. The walls are lined wi hundreds ay leather-bound volumes. A grandfather clock stands in the far corner tick tockin. There's a paintin oan the wall – a fox bein chased by a group ay redcoats on horseback.

Back in the hallway, ah try another door, then another, then another.

Ah find nothin – just more paintins – more books n freakier furnishin.

Ah take another staircase upward, keepin my finger oan the trigger ay the Brownin. There's a black door marked 'Laboratory'.

Inside, aam greeted wi whitewashed walls. Fluorescent bulbs buzz overhead.   A metal gurney stands at the centre ay the room, laden with medical instruments. There are scalpels, forceps n other implements from the dark ages. Vials ay liquids are stacked in glass cabinets – different acid types – Sulphuric, Hydrochloric. There are other liquids too – embalmin fluid, chloroform, n others ah can't pronounce.

Ah leave the laboratory, continuin down the hallway, drawn tae a large metal door, which groans loudly as it opens. The room is dark. Ah fumble at the wall, searchin for the light switch, but can't find it.

Suddenly, the lights burst oan. A scream ay horror freezes in mah lungs. Aam confronted wi mah worst nightmare.

Oh, Christ nae!

The girl stares at me through the glass cubicle. At first ah thought she could be alive, but no one could live wi these injuries. She lies on her front, nailed tae a wooden crucifix. Her head is tilted upward – mouth silently screamin. She is naked, except for a leather strip draped across her back.

Is it mah imagination or is the leather movin? Ah step forward tae get a better look, but when ah put mah hand oan the glass, the leather seemingly disintegrates as a horde ay flies separate n disperse, revealin hungry maggots feastin oan raw, skinless flesh.

A've seen this girl before – oan the news….in mah dreams. Oh Anne–Marie, my poor wee lassie – what has he done tae ye?

Ah take a step back, lookin around the room. There are more glass cubicles, stretchin far as the eye can see.

More dead girls than ah can count.

Now aam feelin sae foolish.

This whole set up – the monastery, the girls – this must have been goin oan for years.

This is beyond madness – beyond evil. Aam way out ay mah depth – ah should have called this in n had a thousand coppers swarmin all over this place. But they wouldn't have believed me, would they? Ah should've made them believe, but mah arrogance convinced me ah could crack this case oan mah own.

A've got tae get out ay here n expose this horror.

Ah move tae the door but suddenly aam feelin woozy – almost fallin over, chuckin up mah guts.

What's that noise comin from the far side ay the room? That dull thud ay flesh poundin against thick glass. Now a've got the image ay a mutilated zombie girl punchin her way from a transparent tomb. Don't be stupid – those sort ay things dinnae happen in the real world.

Glass shatters – followed by the slap ay clammy skin oan stone.

What is that – footsteps? There's somethin wrong wi them – sounds like a hobbled limb draggin along the floor.

Somethin crawls oan mah skin – feels like aam covered in lice.

Ah look at mah hands. Nothin there.

Get yerself together, ye fuckin pussy – this is all in yer head. Then why is that draggin limb gettin louder? Someone or somethin is comin for me.

Ah stumble from the room, takin the stairs down tae the floor below. The lumberin thing continues its pursuit – gatherin pace.

Ah spin around.

Nothin! Yer losin it...yer losin it. This is all in yer mind. Then why do ah have this terrible feelin, as though the devil himself is followin me?

Ah think about Snakeskin Eddie lyin in that hospital bed wi his eyes gouged out n his bollocks chopped off. That gets me movin faster, but the footsteps keep pace. They're right oan top ay me.

Mah legs feel hollow. The hallway spins. Ah almost fall over. Up ahead, ah see the stairs leadin tae the basement, the open window n the outside world.

Ah want tae look over mah shoulder – tae see what's stalkin me. Sae why don't ye turn around n take a little peek? Because ah don't want tae see that decomposin teenage girl crawlin after me, pullin herself along with nail-less fingers.

Ah descend the stone stairwell, trippin oan the bottom step, fallin forward, slammin mah shoulder intae the heavy wooden door. Ah try n turn the metal handle, mindful of the spike that had almost amputated mah hand earlier, but it willnae move. Panic fills me as ah hear the wet slap ay bare feet oan stone above me.....now oan the stairs.

Ah push the door again, usin mah whole body weight – it gives slightly, openin a small crack.

– Come oan, yer bastard! ah scream, pushin harder now. The hinges moan or at least ah pray it's the hinges.

Nae, there's nothin there – just mah imagination playin games. A've almost convinced mahself ay this when ah hear another footstep – that one sounded close – barely two metres away. Now, ah hear ragged breathin – the unnervin sound ay air bein slurped through rotten n decayed lungs, strugglin for breath.

There is nothin there, there is nothin there, sae how come that human-shaped shadow is cast oan the wall n gettin larger? Why is that hand reachin toward me, with long, spider-legged fingers outstretched. The hairs oan mah neck stand, anticipatin its cold, leperous touch.

There is another laboured breath – more like a pained squeal, as though the act itself brings terrible, death wishin agony.

Ah feel warm stinkin breath in mah ear n hear a coarse whisper from a shredded oesophagus.

– Pleeeeeease heeeeeelp me!

The words are barely discernible, but ah definitely heard them. Ah imagine them spoken from the remnants of a severed tongue, leakin decomposin bodily fluids, strugglin to form words.

Ah push wi all my strength. Wood grinds against stone. The gap opens up further – enough for me tae squeeze through? Ah throw mahself intae the openin. Aam almost through when mah leg gets stuck!

What the fu......Oh, mah God! Somethin is holdin mah ankle...there is actually somethin holdin ontae me.

That isnae possible. There is nothin there. But ah can feel skinny fingers around mah ankle.

Then I hear that horrible voice again....

– Kiiiiiiiillllll me, Jack! Pleeeeeeeeeseee kiiiiillllll me!

This is all in yer head. If this thing is real, then how come it knows yer name?

Mah leg comes free n ah pull mahself through the gap before scramblin tae mah feet, catchin a glimpse ay somethin – a black shape tryin tae follow me through.

Ah slam the door, pressin mah weight against it, fearful ay somethin turnin the handle.

But nothin does.

Ah listen but can't hear anythin over the poundin ay my heart n the blood rocketin through mah ears. Everythin trembles. Aam havin a fuckin heart attack.

Calm down! Calm down! It's all over now. You're safe. Ye just need tae get out.

Ah turn around. That's when ah see the shrouded figure standin in front ay the open window, blockin mah exit from the monastery. It wears a red cloak wi a cowl n stands wi hands clasped together, skinny fingers interlocked, as if in prayer. It has two arms n two legs, but that is where any similarity tae humanity ends.

This isnae a man – it is a horrible man–shaped thing.

– I've been waiting for you to come, it says. – You've been looking for me for a long while now, haven't you? Did you see what I did to Anne–Marie? She called out for her mother when I removed her flesh. You should have heard her. It was beautiful.

Oh, mah God! Ah want tae be away from this abomination. Somethin pulls me backward. Ah imagine cancerous tumours pushin against mah skin, as though they might burst from mah back in a desperate attempt tae escape this monster.

The Man Shaped Thing senses mah fear. Cruel laughter fills the chamber.

Ah look down at the Brownin in mah sweaty grasp.

Sergeant Cole screams in mah head.

Just blow the motherfucker's head off, Private, he says.

It should be easy enough – ah used tae hit a bullseye from one hundred metres, but there's only one problem.

Mah hand willnae move.

Transcript of the sworn testimony of Colonel Carl E. Coombs.

GRANT: Colonel, you were the commanding officer on Operation Weeping Willow, is that correct?

COOMBS: I was.

GRANT: And did you work closely with Dr Sebastian Reinhardt?

COOMBS: Not really. Dr Reinhardt didn't work closely with anyone. He was a law unto himself.

GRANT: And what was the purpose of Operation Weeping Willow?

COOMBS: The operation had one clear objective: To create the perfect soldier.

GRANT: How would you define the perfect soldier?

COOMBS: The criteria were varied.

GRANT: Please try and summarise for us.

COOMBS: Increased strength, agility, endurance, the ability to ignore pain.

GRANT: Am I hearing this correctly, Colonel Coombs? You were attempting to create super soldiers. Surely this is something you would only read in science fiction novels or crazed conspiracy theories. Are we really supposed to believe this?

COOMBS: I don't expect you to believe anything.

GRANT: So, who authorised this operation?

COOMBS: Weeping Willow was a joint funded operation between the Ministry of Defence and another government agency, which I am unable to disclose at this time.

GRANT: Colonel, you are aware that everyone present here today has been designated with security clearance level Alpha?

COOMBS: As I said, I am unable to disclose the requested information at this time.

GRANT: So, going back to these super soldiers, how were you planning to create them exactly?

COOMBS: You would need to speak to Dr Reinhardt about the exact procedure.

GRANT: Nothing would give me greater pleasure but as you know, Dr Reinhardt is incapable of appearing at these proceedings, so you will have to fill in as best as you can.

COOMBS: We picked subjects with exceptional physical and mental attributes. These subjects were then exposed to various tests.

GRANT: Could you please describe the nature of these tests to the court? And please remember that you are under oath.

COOMBS: Some were subjected to extreme cold. Others were starved or denied water for extended periods. Most would undergo what we called EPT.

GRANT: EPT?

COOMBS: Extreme Pain Training.

GRANT: And what would this Extreme Pain Training consist of?

COOMBS: Waterboarding, pulling fingernails, electroshocks, tooth extractions, beatings.

GRANT: These men were tortured?

COOMBS: I suppose so.

GRANT: And what was to be gained from torturing these men?

COOMBS: Reinhardt believed that if an individual were put through enough significant trauma, he could create a break in their psyche.

GRANT: A break?

COOMBS: A split personality. Reinhardt believed this could be utilized on the battlefield.

GRANT: Would you care to elaborate?

COOMBS: If the subject were to be wounded or tortured, the split personality would take over and experience any subsequent pain or trauma, while keeping the subject safe or unharmed.

GRANT: Did these horrendous experiments even work?

COOMBS: Yes, subjects were able to operate in combat scenarios with severe and debilitating injuries. In addition, they were not bound by the same physical limitations of their hosts. Many exhibited superhuman strength, and considerable improvements in reaction time and agility.

GRANT: If the operation was such a success, why did you request a transfer from Weeping Willow?

COOMBS: It became clear to me that we weren't creating soldiers. We were creating something else.

GRANT: And what was that?

COOMBS: Monsters. You see, the enhanced physical prowess and pain resistance came with an unfortunate side effect.

GRANT: Namely?

COOMBS: The split personalities did not have the same moral doctrines as their hosts. They were not constrained by the concept of right and wrong. They were psychopaths.

GRANT: And was Michael Coates one of these psychopaths?

COOMBS: No, he was not. Psychopath implies some level of humanity. Mickey didn't qualify.

GRANT: And do you think this other personality might have been responsible for the incident that took place on 2nd January of this year?

COOMBS: It's possible.

GRANT: I would like to remind the court that on 2nd January, Michael Coates walked into the Ministry of Defence office armed with two highly powered automatic rifles and gunned down thirty-one innocent people. I put it to you, Colonel Coombs that you were complicit in his crime. You have blood on your hands.

COOMBS: I don't accept that.

GRANT: But you have already confirmed that you allowed Dr Reinhardt to work unchecked.

COOMBS: It amazes me that we're discussing this now.

GRANT: How so?

COOMBS: Tell me, Mr. Grant. Were they Mickey's first victims? Why was there no investigation into the murder of Dr Reinhardt and his colleagues? Why weren't you asking your questions when Mickey was in far-away lands, feeding dictators their own guts? You weren't looking for explanations until civilians got killed and it was splashed all over the papers. Pardon my French, but you didn't give a fuck about Mickey until then.

GRANT: And why do you think Michael Coates targeted Dr Reinhardt and the Ministry of Defence?

COOMBS: I have no idea. Who knows what was going through his head.

GRANT: I put it to you, Colonel that his motive was revenge. Michael Coates was tracking down the people who created him. If he'd been allowed to continue his killing spree, I have no doubt that he would have eventually worked his way to you. After all, you oversaw this terrible failure of a project, and now, you are trying to absolve yourself of any responsibility. Isn't that correct?

COOMBS: Excuse me, but who said Weeping Willow was a failure?

GRANT: Of course, it was a failure, Colonel. You were supposed to create soldiers, but instead, you created freaks.

COOMBS: I admit most subjects were unable to control their split personalities, but not all.

GRANT: Are you saying that you were successful? You managed to create the perfect soldier?

COOMBS: Yes, there was one.

Joe

Everything in Ashenridge is old and rusted, so the shiny Renault sticks out like a sore thumb. There is nothing inside except an empty packet of Rothmans cigarettes and an open map on the front passenger seat.

I follow mud trodden footprints through the village, which was evacuated during World War Two.

The population never returned.

Can't say I blame them. There is something deeply insidious about this place. Is that the laughter of school children I hear as I cross the abandoned playground of the primary school?

Nothing to worry about – just ghosts of the past.

The footprints lead straight to the monastery and circle the building. Someone trying not to be seen – definitely professional, most likely military. Who are they and what are they doing here? Does it matter? It doesn't change my reason for being here: get inside that building and kill everyone – slowly.

The footprints stop at an open basement window. I lean down and look into the gloom. Can't see or hear anything.

I drop down, half expecting an alarm to trigger, but nothing happens – no sirens blare, no lights flash.

Everything is disconcertingly still.

I instantly recognise the chamber and altar table from Wiebrich's sickening home video. I wonder if Becky was also killed here. Her mutilated face pops into my mind, and my fists curl into balls.

I'm going to make those bastards suffer for what they did to you.

I try the wooden door to my right and cut myself on a spike hidden under the metal ring handle.

What sick fuck designed that – Vlad the Impaler? For fuck's sake, I'm bleeding all over the place.

The door opens, and I take stone steps to the floor above. The décor reminds me of the house in Curzon Street – Horse and Hound meets Metal Hammer magazine. Every room in the corridor is empty, so I head upstairs, where I find the worst room in the entire world.

So many girls – all of them horribly mutilated and displayed in glass cubicles like horrifying art exhibits. Each cubicle is adorned with a gold plaque embossed with the victim's name and the date they joined this ghastly collection. My God – there must be hundreds of them – some dating back to 1950. So much death – this is all too much. I touch my forehead. I'm sweating!

The lights overhead become brighter – more vivid. I have an uncontrollable urge to run from this room, but my legs give beneath me, and now I'm on my hands and knees, drool hanging from my lips.

– What's the matter with me? I ask out loud.

The building answers with a cruel, sadistic laugh, echoing all around. Footsteps close from multiple directions.

– We're coming to get you, a horrible, gloating voice calls out.

Somehow, I'm up on my feet and stumbling from the room, collapsing into the hallway.

The footsteps get closer. I can barely move. My breathing is laboured. Got to hide, but my body is shutting down. It takes every ounce of strength to open the door of the 'Laboratory' opposite. Once inside, I collapse, pulling myself along the floor with my hands.

A silhouette moves on the other side of the wall. It runs skinny, elongated fingers over the frosted partition, staring down at me, tapping on the glass with talon-like fingernails.

Tap tap tap.

Another creature joins it. I see sharp teeth and pointed, Spock-like ears. They look like demons. Don't be silly, Joey, demons don't exist. There is no Heaven, there is no Hell. These creatures are flesh, and they bleed like everything else.

The door handle turns slowly, and they slink into the room, bare-chested, proudly bearing scarred gashes where their nipples had once been. No, these aren't demons – they're men, but hideously mutilated – with teeth filed down and ears carved into points. Both carry long, serrated blades, and they look eager to use them.

– Can we kill him now, Master? one of them asks.

I turn my head. Someone stands over me. He wears the same gold mask, crimson robe, and priest's cassock he'd been wearing in Wiebrich's video.

How did he get behind me without me seeing him? Is he a ghost? He's no ghost – that mirrored wall must be a hidden door. I give these freaks ten out of ten for theatrics.

– Please, Master, let me kill him! the goblin says, carrying a prominent bulge in his skin-tight leather trousers.

– Not yet, Red Robe says. – Search him!

Skinny fingers rummage through my pockets.

– He's only carrying this, The Goblin says, handing Red Robe the marker pen from my pocket.

Red Robe inspects it briefly before tossing it away.

– How are you feeling, my brave little interloper? Feeling a bit wonky, are we?

– What did you do to me?

– It's quite disconcerting, isn't it – not being in control of your own body? What you're feeling is the effect of a psychotropic compound called EZA. Technically, it doesn't exist, but I'm able to procure it from one of our military contacts. The effects vary greatly depending on dosage, but they can include hallucinations, paralysis, and even death.

– How did you?

– Administer it? Into your bloodstream.

I look at the bloody gash in my palm.

– You catch on quick! Red Robe says. – You must be pretty tough because you should be peeling your face off given the dose you've had. I suppose I'll have to do that myself.

He holds up a pair of surgical scissors, opening and closing the blades.

Snip snip.

– Please, I say.

– Don't waste your breath begging. Not yet anyway. There will be plenty of time for that. You're going to be my masterpiece. There will be no end to your suffering. You think you are the first person to try and bring down the Wiebrichs? Our name has blazed a bloody trail through history. Did you really think you could come in here with your marker pen and hope to challenge us?

They all start laughing – mocking me, so I start laughing too – exaggerated laughter that makes my ribs hurt.

Red Robe and his two gimps look at each other uncertainly.

– What are you laughing at? Red Robe asks. – Do you think you'll still be laughing when I've cut out your tongue and stitched your lips together?

I keep laughing. – You think you're so fucking powerful, don't you? Do you want me to show you how powerful you are?

Somewhere deep inside, a key turns and everything goes dark. I lose time and when I'm back in the real world, a goblin lies at my feet – his head is twisted around one eighty degrees so he's admiring his own arse.

The other goblin jerks in my grasp. A horrific wound is cut into his throat, which his tongue has been pulled through, fashioning a gruesome necktie. When he stops twitching, I let him drop to the floor.

Red Robe stands motionless, seemingly unable to comprehend how things have changed so significantly.

– Tobias Wiebrich, I presume.

Red Robe removes his mask, revealing a face I've seen before. He's the spit of his evil ancestor, the infamous Elias Wiebrich, who vanished all those centuries ago.

– What are you? he asks me, voice trembling.

I pick up my marker pen and flick off the lid. – Let me show you!

CONFESSIONS OF MR X??

Forgive me, Father, for I have sinned, it has been forever since my last confession.

When I was at school, I was different from the other kids. I never really connected with anyone. Most people thought I was shy, but the truth is, there was something wrong with me. I would lie awake at night thinking about the ways I wanted to hurt people, including my own mother and father. I wasn't a psychopath. I knew the difference between right and wrong, so I never acted on these urges but that didn't stop the dark thoughts in my head.

By the time I was sixteen, my desires had grown into something truly terrifying. I realised it was only a matter of time before I killed someone, so I figured I might as well get paid for it. I went to the local army recruiting office and signed up.

After extensive psychological tests, a doctor came and asked if I wanted to volunteer for a special tactical unit. We would be going to the places no one wanted to go, killing the evil bastards no one wanted to fuck with.

I accepted immediately.

What I didn't know was the training would almost kill me. Those bastards subjected me to pain I didn't think possible. No doubt, you're wondering why that dose of EZA had little or no effect on me. They pumped me full of that shit for two whole years, just to see what it would do to me and now – well, the smell just makes me feel nostalgic.

Do you want to know why they did all that to me? They wanted to create a voice in my head – an alter ego capable of something monstrous.

And they thought they succeeded, but that isn't the truth. What they didn't know and what I have never admitted to anyone, until now, was that the voice was always there – always talking to me, as long as I can remember.

You see, I am the monster, and I am also the creator.

This is my confession.

Now, Father, you are probably wondering why I have tied you to this operating table and drawn one thousand lines on your body. Each line represents a cut I'm going to make with this scalpel. They ensure I don't accidentally nick an artery because I don't want you bleeding out too soon. You see, you're going to be my masterpiece. There will be no end to your suffering. And please, no begging – there'll be plenty of time for that.

And just to make sure you don't miss anything, the first cuts I'll make will be the ones at the top of your eyelids, but I promise I'll let you keep your testicles right until the end.

Now – shall we begin.

Joe

After two days, I am finished with Tobias. His heart eventually gave out – there's only so much trauma the human body can take before it gives out.

I walk through the abandoned monastery – desperate to get out into the fresh air, to rid myself from the stench of death.

That's when I see the body.

The man has been nailed to the wall – his stomach excavated, shredded intestines hanging like bloody tendrils. There is something strangely familiar about him. I'm sure I've seen him somewhere before, but I can't remember where.

I look into his face – he looks peaceful – at rest. The mud on his shoes tell me he'd been responsible for the muddy tracks I'd followed earlier.

Who was he and what was he doing here? I know him from somewhere. I've seen that raincoat before.

Fuck it! I don't care who he is. I'm not sure I care about anything anymore.

CATFORD, SOUTH LONDON. 1989.

Benny runs round the livin room with his arms outstretched, makin whooshin noises. He's wearin his Superman costume repeatin: 'Is it a bird, is it a plane' over an over.

– What the fuck are you so excited about? I ask im.

– It's Christmas, he replies.

– So fuckin what?

– Presents! Presents!

Presents? He's gotta be fuckin kiddin! Don't he remember last year, or the year before? If he's lucky, he won't get another kickin or late night visit from The Ghoul. I dunnt old out much hope for an appy Christmas myself, but I gotta admit the Christmas tree is new. I'd almost choked on my Snicker's bar when The Ghoul'd dragged it into the lounge. It weren't no tiddler either – must be at least six foot.

Fuck knows where he got it. He must've fuckin nicked it from sumwhere. There's no way he'd spend his ard earned dole money on anythin other than bettin slips or bad bourbon. He'd even bought tinsel an fairy lights – very unusual behavior. Maybe he's started takin drugs – whatever it is, I ope he keeps takin it.

Mum walks in, smilin – even she's been appier than normal – must be sumfin goin around.

– Are you just going to sit there watching telly? she asks me.

– What else do you want me to do?

– Your Dad asked you to finish decorating the tree.

– He ain't my fuckin dad, I say.

– Please don't start. I want us to have a normal Christmas.

Normal! You're shacked up with a psycho kiddy fiddler who's noncein on your eleven-year-old son. There ain't no normal – not for any of us – not no more. I wonder if I should tell her. Who am I kiddin? She already knows – she just don't wanna face facts.

The front door slams downstairs. The Ghoul calls out.

– Honey, I'm home!

– Hey honey – we're upstairs, Mum replies.

– Come down ere an give me an and, will ya!

– Why, what have you got? Mum asks excitedly.

– That'd be tellin now, wouldn't it?

Mum eads downstairs. Moments later, they both enter the living room, carryin parcels wrapped in sparkly paper.

I can't believe my fuckin eyes. Benny was right. The Ghoul has only gone out an bought presents. I'm tempted to pinch myself to make sure I ain't dreamin.

The Ghoul lays a large rectangular package at my feet.

– Fuck me, that's eavy, he says. – Merry Christmas, Clay!

– This is for me?

– That's what the tag says, dunnt it?

I check an sure enough, there's my name.

– Go ahead an open it! he says, slumpin onto the sofa opposite.

I look at Mum – she looks deliriously appy, shakin a small package next to er ear. – What is it – jewellery? she asks.

– Just open it!

– But it isn't Christmas day yet.

– I know, The Ghoul says with a wink. – I won't tell Santa if you dunnt.

– Don't I have one? Benny asks, sulkily.

– Of course, it's over there, he says, pointin to a square box on the floor.

Benny skips over an starts unwrappin.

– That's my boy, The Ghoul says. – Now come on, the rest of you – you're hurtin my feelins.

I feel The Ghoul watchin as I pull at wrappin paper. He's got this strange look on his face – like he's eard the funniest joke ever but is tryin not to laugh.

– What the fuck is this? I say when I've finished.

– It's a coffin! he says.

– I can see it's a coffin.

– What's the matter – don't ya like it?

– No, I don't fuckin like it!

– Well, you ain't given it a chance yet. Why dunnt you get in an give it a spin?

He's got a real odd look on his face now. I'm tryin not to show it, but he's really givin me the creeps. Mum's equally freaked out – she's opened up her box an is holdin a knife coated in dried blood.

What the fuck?

Now Benny is cryin his eyes out, screamin like he's seen the most orrible thing ever.

I get up from the sofa, lookin down at the box he just opened. The severed head of a young woman stares back at me.

I back away as The Ghoul gets to his feet.

– What's the matter, Benny, dunnt ya like your present? He lifts the head by long blonde hair. – This is the social worker your bitch-whore mother called to take you away from me. Ain't that right, Sharon?

– What have you done? Mum says, backin up against the wall, draggin Benny wiv her, edgin toward the door.

The Ghoul cuts off their exit an smacks er in the face.

Wivout finkin, I swing at him. – You fuckin cocksucker!

He sees me comin an cracks me in the stomach so ard I sink to my knees. Then he smacks me in the face an now my cheek touches carpet. He kicks me in the chest over an over, roarin as my ribs break.

– Get off him! Benny shrieks, pullin at his trousers.

The Ghoul carries him into the hallway. – Look, it's a little Super'ero! You wanna be like Superman, do you? If you wanna be like Superman, you gotta learn to fly. Let me give you a flyin lesson!

He flings Benny headfirst down the stairs. I hear a thud when he hits the floor.

The Ghoul comes back into the room, glarin at Mum. – This is your fault, bitch, he says. – All you ad to do was keep yer mouth shut, but you decided to get fuckin clever, dinnt ya?

– What did you expect? You were hurting my babies!

– Well, both your babies are gonna fuckin die cos a' your fuckin stupidity.

– No! Mum screams, slashin his cheek with the knife.

The Ghoul steps back, casually examinin the wound in the mirror on the wall.

Then he goes fuckin nuts.

– You shouldn't ave done that, you fuckin ore! He kicks Mum full in the face, knockin teeth out. Then he's on top a' er, punchin over an over.

I crawl toward im. – Get off er! You leave er alone or I'll fuckin kill you!

The Ghoul climbs off Mum, startin toward me. – Still a fuckin tough guy, eh!

He lifts me an squeezes my ribs. Sumfin goes in my back, an now I can't move, fallin limply to the floor.

The Ghoul moves back to Mum, leans down an picks up the knife.

– You leave er alone, or I'm gonna fuckin kill you!

He laughs at me. – I just popped two a' your vertebrae. You can't even walk – now watch this closely.

The Ghoul slices Mum's throat an watches as she jerks on the floor, clawin at the wound. Now he's on top a' her, sawin with the knife. Steel slices thru skin an muscle. Mum's breaths turn into horrible rasps when the blade goes fru er windpipe.

I want to turn away, but I can't move. I spose I could close my eyes, but I can't. Sumfin keeps me watchin.

It takes a long time before he is done. When he's finished, he picks up Mum's ead an olds it up in front a' me.

– Look, she's even more fuckin ugly now! he says.

– I swear to God, I'm gonna fuckin kill you!

– You said that before. You really shouldn't make promises you can't keep. A man should always keep his word, you remember that.

Then he grabs my ankles an drags me across the carpet.

– What are you goin to do with me?

– Sssssh, he says. – You've got your whole life behind ya now.

Clay

– This is a waste of my fucking time! Spivey says to me.

– Will you shut up an keep shovellin!

– It's fucking raining!

– A little bit a' water never urt nobody.

We've been diggin for fifteen minutes an Spivey has been moanin fourteen minutes an fifty-nine seconds of em.

– Let's just cut their throats and get out of here, he says.

– I said, keep diggin!

We're almost halfway now – free foot down – just another free to go. I'm so excited. It's been so long since anyone rolled a five... When was the last time? It must have been... no, I really shouldn't fink about that. That was the last time I intentionally broke my word. I ain't proud a' that, but I'm only human at the end a' the day.

I can't wait to see Gabby's face when I put Laura in the ground. I might even make her fill in the grave – shovel dirt onto her own daughter while she's still breathin. But how would I get her to do it? That bitch has got some fight in er. I'd have to get creative, but I'm sure I could find a way if I pressed the right buttons.

– I've had enough of this shit, Spivey says, throwin his shovel to the ground, wipin rainwater from his eyes. – I'm going back inside.

– You do as you're told, or I'll wrap this shovel round yer fuckin ead.

– Go ahead and try it – see what happens, you faggot!

– What did you call me, ya greasy little cunt? I ain't no fuckin homo!

– No, that's why you like fucking little boys, isn't it? Course you're a homo – you prick!

– Call me a homo again an see what happens!

– Homo homo homo!

– I'm gonna rip your fuckin throat out!

Spivey raises his fists. – Come on then! I always wanted to fight you, Clay. I wanna see how tough you really are!

– You dumb cunt! There ain't a man alive who can take me in a fight!

I take two steps forward an I'm about to wipe his face from his ead when the shotgun blast comes from the ouse.

Gabby

Danny paces the room nervously. Before he and Spivey had gone outside, Clay had ordered him to watch us, but he doesn't want to be here. His hand trembles and knocks against his leg.

There is weakness here – weakness we need to exploit.

– Danny, please help us, Laura says. – Do you hear me? We need your help.

– I can't, he says, on the verge of tears.

– You know he's going to kill us, don't you? I say. – He's going to bury my daughter alive, and then he's going to kill me. Is that what you want?

– No!

– You know what he is, don't you? He's a monster. He's going to kill us, just like he killed Josh and just like he killed Kirsty. Did you enjoy watching them die? Did it get you off?

He stares at me with frenzied eyes. – Why are you saying this?

– I'm trying to understand why you're helping him.

– I'm not helping him!

– Yes, you are! You're helping him right now by watching us. Do you know Laura's pregnant?

Danny's eyes lower to Laura's belly. – She's pregnant? he asks hesitantly, unsure whether to believe me.

– That's right. How does it feel to be a baby killer?

He's crying now. – I don't want any of this.

– Then prove it! Undo these cuffs and let us go.

– I can't! He'll hurt me.

– Does he often hurt you? You know you don't have to stay with him. We can all escape together.

– There is no escape. Don't you get it? Wherever we go, he'll find us. He always does.

– If you keep us here, we'll die. You have to help us.

– I can't. I don't even have the key.

– You could help us break the pipe.

– I can't help you at all!

– Then you've killed us. You're nothing more than a dirty little murderer.

– Please don't say that! he says with a whimper.

I scream at him. – Murderer! Murderer!

He covers his ears and runs from the room.

I scream louder. – Danny, you can't leave us here!

– What did you do that for? Laura asks. – You chased him away!

– I had to try something! I reply, looking at the clock on the wall. How long will it take those freaks to dig a Laura-sized hole? It's my job to protect her, but here I am – chained to this radiator and completely useless.

And what about Ben – my poor Ben? What if he's still alive, out in the cold, writhing in pain? Maybe he's calling out my name, waiting for me to find him.

I close my eyes and squeeze the image from my mind. I look at the photograph on the floor – our perfect family and I think about the perfect future these bastards have ripped from us.

Tears well, but I hold them back.

The minute hand moves.

I think about all the years Ben and I have spent together – all the times we stayed up drinking, listening to music. He is the love of my life. I can't leave him to die. And now I hear Jennifer Rush's The Power of Love in my head.

I bet Jennifer wouldn't give up. She wouldn't sit by and let everything she cared about be destroyed. She wouldn't let anything happen to her man. No, she would do whatever it took, no matter how foolish the solution.

I pick up the photograph and smash the glass frame. Then I slice through the webbing between my thumb and forefinger, with a glass shard.

Laura screams at me. – What are you doing? Are you fucking crazy?

Soon, I'm into the joint, chopping through muscle and ligament. The pain is indescribable.

Laura tries to stop me, but I push her off, continuing to cut – back and forth.

The retarded brother walks in. He must've heard the commotion. He stares at me, completely puzzled at what I'm trying to do. Dribble runs from his lips as he laughs at me. You, dumb shit, I think to myself.

Steel touches bone. I can't cut anymore, so I bend my thumb back until the joint snaps like a wishbone. Blood spurts and soaks into the carpet. I feel woozy, as though I'm about to be sick.

With one final cut, I sever the last remaining shred of skin that keeps my thumb attached to my hand. I slide the cuff off.

Benny's eyes bulge with panic. He yells out his brother's name, but I'm up on my feet, flying at him with the glass shard raised. He plucks me from mid-air, giggling as he dumps me on the floor, wrapping an enormous hand around my throat. I try to fight him but he's too strong. He squeezes. I can't breathe.

Laura pulls at his hair, raking his eyes and face with her nails. I take my opportunity and thrust the glass upward, straight into his Adam's apple. He falls to the side, feebly fumbling for the glass, trying to pull it free.

I give him a helping hand and rip it from his neck. Blood shoots out, showering me as I jump on top of him, bringing the blade down over and over. He lets out an awful gurgled scream, but I don't stop.

I see Josh's and Ben's faces as I stab.

I think about the slasher films I watched when I was younger, where the female would–be victim would get the upper hand on the killer, usually by stabbing him in the leg and would foolishly decide not to finish him off when he was at her mercy. That leniency would always come back to bite her on the arse. Well, that's not happening here!

I stab Benedict in the throat. I stab him in the face. I stab him in the eyes. I stab until he no longer bucks beneath me – until his legs stop twitching.

When I'm finished, I look up and see Danny pointing his pistol at me with shaky hands.

– What did you do? he says.

Then I'm deafened by a shotgun blast and Danny is no longer there. I turn to see Laura holding the shotgun. Her body trembles. Twin barrels smoke.

– I thought he was going to shoot you, she says.

I throw my arms around her. – It's okay. You did what you had to. We have to get out of here. The others will have heard the shot.

Laura bends down and prizes the pistol from Danny's hand. – Screw that, she says. – We've got two guns now. Let's wait for them and let them have it when they come through the door.

I consider that. Could it work? I look out of the back window – Clay and Spivey creep toward the house with weapons drawn. Decision time – fight or flee? Could we take them? It doesn't seem likely. They were trained killers and I'm badly wounded.

– No, we make a break for it, I say. – These men may be tough, but they don't know the woods – not like we do.

– But Mum!

– We don't have time to argue!

I pick up a handful of shotgun shells and stuff them into my trouser pocket as we run out of the front door and into the woods.

Branches claw our skin and clothes. My hand hurts like hell. I've never known pain like it. It feels like we're running for an hour before we hit the pathway leading to the main road.

– What are you doing? Laura asks when she sees I'm no longer following her. – We've got to move.

– I'm not coming with you.

– What are you talking about?

– I need to find your father.

– He's dead. You heard what that fucker said.

– We don't know he's dead. He could still be alive. I have to try and find him.

– Then I'm coming with you.

– No, you have to go. You have to think about your baby now.

– We should stick together.

– This is something I have to do. Now give me the shotgun, it'll only slow you down.

– Please don't do this, Mum. I need you!

I wrap my arms around her and kiss her forehead. – You have to run baby – you run, and you don't stop running until you find someone to pick you up on the road.

Her face is swollen with tears – she doesn't move, so I forcibly turn and shove her, but still, she doesn't run.

I scream at her. – Go! You, stupid bitch!

That makes her move. She takes hesitant steps before breaking into a sprint.

She turns back once before the darkness swallows her.

I would've done anything to go with her – to make sure she made it safely to the road, but I can't run anymore. I've lost so much blood I can barely stand. I'd only slow her down and she'd never leave me if I told her the truth.

I squeeze my hand hard. Blood wells up from the wound, puddling on the floor. Got to give these fuckers some breadcrumbs to follow – lead them away from my baby.

Then I take the path in the other direction, leading to Margaret's cottage.

Clay

Danny an Benny'd better be all right. Them little bitches better not ave urt em. But ow could they? When I left, they were unarmed an cuffed to a fuckin radiator. Surely even Benny an Danny couldn't fuck that up – could they?

Maybe Danny had grown some balls an shot one a' them when they tried to turn im against me. Or maybe Benny'd accidently blown his face off, mistakin the shotgun for a lollypop. The big dumb fuck. Deep down that fought gives me relief.

Did I really want that orrible, fat land walrus, droolin an gurnin his chops off next to me an Danny on the beach, in our little island paradise? It'd be better if he woz dead. Don't fink fings like that, Clay. He's your bruvva! You gave your word you'd look after him.

I enter the ouse slowly an carefully while Spivey covers me – steppin straight into a slaughterhouse. I'm standin over what appears to be my bruvva, but I can't be a undred percent sure, cos his head looks like mince. I can only tell it's him cos he's got that McDonald's toy car in his and.

What did Benny ever do to deserve this? Sure, he urt kids sometimes, but he didn't know no better. It was just the way he woz wired. And them bitches killed him!

Fuckin ores!

Now Spivey's standin over me, lookin like a little kid who's about to tell his mum he's shat the bed.

– You find Danny? I ask im.

– He's dead, he says, lookin at the floor.

Spivey weren't kiddin. Danny's deader than Rasputin when they fished him outta that frozen lake. The shotgun blast has left a hole in his chest, the size a' my fist. The impact has dry walled him into the livin room.

I lean over an kiss im on the lips. – Now let's find them bitches, I say to Spivey, strugglin to contain the rage buildin inside me.

– Are you fucking kidding me? Let's just take the money and get out of here!

– We don't go nowhere til we find them ores!

– You're gonna get us banged up. We need to leave before the fucking cops come!

– The cops ain't cummin.

– How do you know that?

– I just do!

– They could be miles away from here by now.

– No way. They're on foot – we'll find em.

– In this weather? Fuck that.

– Then don't come, but I'm goin. I gave my word that I would kill anyone who messed with my boys. You want me to break my word?

– You're going to get us locked up for your fucking word?

– I told you, the police ain't cummin, but you leave if you want.

He gives me a suspicious look. – With my share of the money?

– Yeah take it, I say, kickin one a' the sports bags. – But if you walk out that door, then me and you are done. You don't get no passport or flight out the country. How long you fink it'll be before the police pick you up? You elp me an then we get out a' ere together.

Spivey looks uncertain, but he's headin toward the door. – Okay, let's go, he says.

We ead outside. The wind has died down. The rain has stopped. You don't need to be no Navahoe tracker to follow the mud trodden footprints an the sperm–thick splatter a' blood reflectin in the moonlight. One of em must be badly urt. I ope not too bad – I don't want em dyin on me before I get old of em.

We follow the tracks until they split off in two different directions. One leads toward the main road, the other one turns back in the direction of the withered bitch's cottage.

– What do you wanna do? Spivey asks, examinin the footprints.

– You follow them. I'll take these ones.

– Why don't we just get out of here?

– Because I want em. I want em now! You bring that bitch back to me an you bring er back un'armed.

– Are you serious?

– I'm fuckin serious! I'm gonna make both a' them pay for what they've taken from me. You do this an you get Danny's an Benny's share a' the money.

That brings a sadistic clown's smile to Spivey's face. He turns an scurries off.

I take my dice out of my pocket an grind them in my palm..... Then I follow the bloody tracks.

HEADLINE FROM DAILY ARTICLE BY MARK COHEN

KIDNAPPED GIRL'S MUTILATED REMAINS FOUND INSIDE MONSTER MONASTERY

Police discover hundreds of missing girl's bodies.

Britain's biggest mass murder inquiry was believed to be underway last night.

Police scrambled to what was thought to be an abandoned monastery in the deserted ghost town of Ashenridge. What they found inside was more horrific than anything they could have imagined.

Over one hundred dismembered bodies have been discovered, most of which are teenage girls with ages ranging from seventeen to as young as eleven or twelve. Police sources believe that figure will rise as they continue to excavate the foundations of the building.

Meanwhile, the pain—staking process of identifying the victims has already begun, and tragically, police have confirmed that one of the bodies belonged to Anne-Marie Towers, who was abducted while out with friends in Soho last week.

Detective Sergeant Chris Cooper said: "I can confirm that Anne-Marie is one of the victims we have found. Her parents formally identified her remains earlier this morning. We now ask that all members of the press and media give them time to grieve in private. This is obviously a very difficult time for their family".

"An investigation will now begin to ensure that everyone and anyone who was involved in this atrocity will be swiftly and firmly brought to justice. In the meantime, we would urgently like to speak to the anonymous caller who called this in. We believe they will have key information, which will help us understand exactly what happened here. We urge them to come forward whoever or wherever they may be".

Joe

The priest delivers a lovely eulogy. It's a shame I'm the only one to hear it.

When the gravediggers are finished, I leave a dozen long-stemmed roses on Becky's grave and whisper goodbye to my friend.

I place another twelve at the base of Charlotte's headstone and speak out loud. – I'm going away, my little munchkin, and I don't think I'm coming back. I planned to drink myself into that plot next to you, but I don't deserve to spend eternity with you. I've given my plot to Becky. I think you would have liked her. I want you to know that you were the best thing that ever happened to me, and I will always love you.

Next, I move to Toby's grave and lay a teddy bear, proudly bearing the name Hugo across its front in bright blue lettering.

– I hope you can forgive me, little man! You look after my girls for me – okay?

I leave the cemetery, walking straight past the yellow-toothed crone who'd given me a distasteful look when she'd seen the flowers I bought at Liberty's earlier. Then I walk past the Prince of Wales pub without the slightest hankering for a drink.

Back in Soho, I find a phone booth on Dean Street, reeking of piss and plastered with leaflets advertising the services of 'models' you wouldn't touch with a syphilitic cock.

I pick up the receiver and dial. It rings four times before I hear Charlie's voice.

– Hello.

– It's me, I say.

– Of course, it is! I was wondering if I'd hear from you again. I'm glad you called.

– You are?

– Oh yeah. There's something I need to ask you. What have you done, Joey?

– What needed to be done.

– I told you to leave Webrich alone.

– Yeah well, I never was very good at listening, was I? Did you know, Charlie?

– Know what?

– What those bastards were doing with the girls.

– No, but I'm not surprised. He was an evil little cunt. So, what now?

– I'm going on permanent vacation.

– That's what I figured. Did you go to the graveyard and see my sister?

– I did.

– That's good.

– Can I ask you something?

– Of course – you're my brother – you can ask me anything.

– Why did she love me?

– Haven't you figured that out yet? One day you'll understand. You shouldn't need a fuck up like me to explain it to you.

– But I wasn't good enough for her.

– Neither of us were good enough for her. You know they'll come after you, don't you?

– Who's 'they'?

– Everyone! And you know I'll have to come looking for you too?

– I know, Charlie.

– I hope I don't find you.

– Me too. I have to go now. Goodbye, Brother, I say.

There is a brief silence on the line.

– Goodbye, Brother, he replies.

I hang up the phone and twirl Charlotte's engagement ring on my finger. I've gotten so used to wearing it. It's the last connection I have to her other than her grave. The thought of getting rid of it terrifies me but how can I move on with my life if I cling to my painful past.

I approach a young girl huddled in a shop doorway.

– Good morning, Mister, she says with a smile.

I'm amazed by how happy she is, considering her predicament. She was safe for now, but these streets would gobble her up eventually. She would fall into that endless cycle of drink, drugs and possibly prostitution unless something changed. I think about what Becky had said when she'd clocked Charlotte's ring for the first time – *You should give it to someone like me!*

– I have a favour to ask you, I say, offering her a wad of notes – must be close to ten grand.

Her eyes widen. – I'm not a whore, she says.

– Please don't use that word. Anyway, that's not what I want.

– Then what?

– I need you to do something for me. I need you to stay alive. I drop Charlotte's ring into her cupped hand and turn away, crossing the road to the red Mini.

– *Tying off all loose ends, are we? The dead wife, the sociopathic brother–in–law, tight fitting pieces of jewellery – you'll want to get rid of me next.*

That's right. You've kept me alive more times than I want to admit, but I can't take you with me.

– *And where is that?*

I get behind the wheel and open the book on the front passenger seat – England's Most Beautiful Villages. Becky's writing is scrawled across one of the pages: *I think we could be happy here, Joey – what do you think?*

The photographs look beautiful – a picturesque windmill and rolling fields polka-dotted with sheep.

– *What are you going to do there? Become a fucking sheep farmer?*

I'm going to live – for Tommy, for Becky, and for Charlotte.

– *Then I suppose I'd better make myself scarce.*

Are you kidding me? I've spent the last ten years killing myself trying to get rid of you, and all I needed to do was ask politely?

– *Like you said: you don't need me anymore. Besides, I've got better things to do than hang around with a ponce like you.*

– Then I suppose this is goodbye?

I say the words out loud, but there is no reply.

I start up the ignition and look at the page title, noting the name of the village Becky had picked out for us.

– Now, how the fuck do I get to Greybrook? I say.

Gabby

I run through the dark wood. Branches tear my clothes and lash my skin. Tripping over a fallen branch, I reach out and steady myself against a tall oak. My wounded hand doesn't like that one bit. I start moving again, struggling to keep hold of the shotgun, which almost slips from my hands, greasy with blood. I don't think I'm far from Margaret's now – it's so hard to tell in the dark.

A muddy bog pulls at my ankles, sucking me down. This whole night has been one endless nightmare. Stop whining, you silly girl. Remember what you're doing out here! You've got to find Ben, but my legs are freezing up. I scream in frustration. What would Jennifer Rush do? Would she feel sorry for herself? Would she whine about a little hand injury?

No – nothing would stop Jennifer from getting to her man! I bite down and plod through calf-deep sludge.

Up ahead, moonlight penetrates the dense wall of trees, signalling an end to the wood. I come out into a clearing and see the long winding path leading over the hill toward the cottage.

I sense someone behind me, so spin around to see Clay leaned up against an elm tree. He looks like he hasn't got a care in the world. How the hell did he get in front of me?

– Ello, Gabs, I knew I'd find you here. I knew you'd come for your usband.

My finger twitches against the trigger of the shotgun.

– Come on, let's not do anything silly. We both know I could blow your ead off ten times over, before you get a chance to fire that fing.

– I'm game, why don't we find out?

He smiles and stares at my thumbless hand. – Look what you've done to yourself, Gabs. I gotta say, I really underestimated you. You've got real strength – strength I didn't fink you ad. I really admire you.

– I'm really fucking flattered! I've always wanted to be admired by an inadequate, murdering psycho.

– Careful, Gabby!

– Or what – you'll kill me? What's the matter, does the truth hurt? Don't you like hearing that you're an evil freak? I've been wondering how someone becomes such a weirdo. Did Mummy not cuddle you enough or did Daddy cuddle you too much?

His demeanor changes. Suddenly he's looking very uncomfortable. I've touched a nerve. I smell blood, so I continue biting.

– That's it, isn't it? Your dad fucked you, so you've got to fuck everyone else, you sad little man!

– What are you tryin to do? You want me to kill you quickly, is that it? Maybe you fink you're buyin time for that little girl a' yours? I got some bad news for you – I sent Spivey after her an he's gonna bring her back to me. She's goin in the ground while she's still breathin for what you done to my boys!

– Fuck you!

– No, fuck you! You fink this is gonna end appily for you? This ain't gonna ave no appy ending. There ain't no ero who's gonna ride over that ill an save the day. This is the end for you.

A million thoughts race through my head – Ben lying out in the cold, bleeding – crying out for me to find him. Now, I see Josh beaten to death in front of my eyes and Spivey stalking my little girl in the darkness.

I pray that she's safe. I know she'll be a wonderful mother. I wish we hadn't spent so many years arguing –

wasting so many hours fighting over trivial things that didn't matter.

And now I'm lifting the shotgun as fast as I can. I'm going to blast this bastard to Kingdom Come.

Laura

He's hunting me.

I can sense him. I can feel his stinking breath on my neck, so I run as fast as I can, leg muscles burning like battery acid. It's been ages since I've done any exercise. Why hadn't I kept my New Year's resolution and used my exorbitant gym membership? If I was in shape, I might've made it to the road already. I could be safe in a car, speeding to the police station.

Life is full of maybes. Maybe if I'd known those evil psychos were going to turn up tonight, I would've bought first-class tickets to Barbados for me and my family. Then this nightmare night would never have happened.

I hope Mum's okay and she's found Dad. I love my parents so much. What will I do without them? What will I do without Josh? He's gone. I'll never get to see his smile again or hear his terrible jokes. My baby will never play with its Dad. Mum would tell me to worry about myself.

I'm not far from the road now. Streetlamps flicker on the horizon.

Another five hundred metres will do it.

Just one more push.

Then I hear Spivey's horrible gloating voice. – Where are you going, Laura?

Oh no! Oh no!

I turn and aim Danny's pistol in the direction of the voice. Spivey laughs – the sound comes from the opposite direction, so I spin around, almost toppling over with panic. He's somewhere in the woods, hidden amongst the trees.

– Come on, Laura – don't leave. I want to play with you!

I pull the trigger, but nothing happens. What the fuck? Could the safety be on? That's what always happens in the movies, isn't it?

Spivey laughs again. – Ah, no bullets – such a shame. You think Clay would give that idiot Danny a loaded gun? It sounds like he's right over my shoulder. Where the hell is he, and what if he's not alone? What if he's distracting me while Clay sneaks up on me?

I whirl around.

Only darkness.

I look back at the streetlamps. They're so close. A car passes – engine roaring. The sound beckons me.

– Why don't you want to play with me, Laura?

Fuck this! I turn and break for the road, legs and arms pumping hard. Lights get closer with every step. Footsteps close in behind me.

He's so close – I can smell the sickness pouring off him. Now I'm on the road and headlights speed toward me. Spivey's so close – heat comes off his hand, reaching for my neck.

The red car is so close now.

Joe

I pull over and look at the A to Z.

This village is impossible to find. The DJ on the radio doesn't help either – his chirpy optimism never lets up even when he reads out depressing news headlines.

The value of the pound hits its lowest value for five years.

Tensions escalate with Russia.

Police have charged a man with slaughtering his own family at a large country residence in Oxfordshire.

I remember when Becky and I had first heard that story on the radio. That seems like a lifetime ago now. Back when I'd been happy.

I start the ignition again. Headlights cut through the night. I drive for ten minutes, and I'm starting to worry I'm lost.

Then I see the sign: Greybrook – 5 miles. Thank fuck for that.

Something up ahead grabs my attention – a tinge of yellow in the dark.

What is that? A young woman in the middle of the road, running toward me, wearing a bright yellow summer dress.

Oh my God! It can't be!

It's Becky!

It can't be though – Becky's dead. I saw her body. I watched her go into the ground. But if she's dead, then how come she's running toward me – her long black hair blowing in the wind, her pale blue eyes sparkling in the moonlight.

She must've come to Greybrook after she'd run away from the hotel. But how? She didn't have any money. Maybe she had her own.

But I saw her body – or did I? I only lifted that sheet for a second before that policeman confronted me – and that girl's face had been mutilated. It could easily have been someone else. My God, it's her! It must be her!

My pulse races. It's so good to see her. I'm so happy.

But why are her eyes wide with panic?

Now I see the man chasing her. I slam the brakes. The car grinds to a halt, and I get out. The pursuer stops dead in his tracks before backing off and disappearing into the trees.

Becky opens up the passenger door and climbs inside the Mini. – Thank you so much for stopping! she says.

I jump back behind the steering wheel and look at her. My heart drops, and my world crumbles to pieces – she looks so much like her, but it isn't Becky. She could be her older twin.

– Are you okay? she asks me.

– Yes, sorry, I say, trying not to cry. – It's just you remind me of someone. Was that guy chasing you?

– Oh, don't worry about him – that's just Dave – the absolute dickhead, I call him.

The DJ talks on the radio.

– *So now we're gonna play a brand-new track that's gone straight into the charts at number six and it's already a personal favourite of mine. This is Jon Waite with Missing You.*

– Oh, I love this song, she says, pulling down the makeup mirror, checking herself out. Then she turns and offers me her hand. – I'm Gabby, by the way!

Ben

PAIN. Intense FUCKING PAIN.

The bullet hole in my gut feels like it's a mile wide. I crawl on my belly, pulling myself along with my hands because my legs no longer work. I'm so tired. My eyes want to close. I roll over – dirt is in the wound. Fuck it! Infection is the least of my worries. At this rate, I'll be dead long before that happens. I press on the wound, trying to stem the blood seeping through my fingers. Moving is the last thing I should be doing, but I've got to get back home and make sure my girls are safe.

Gabby and Laura are all that matters now.

I keep crawling – setting myself targets – metre by metre. Try not to think of the pain.

Then I hear a gunshot up ahead. Sounds like a Beretta, the same Beretta that put me on my arse. It's close – just over that hill. Waves of panic and adrenaline surge through me, giving me a fourth wind.

I drag myself along, using fistfuls of grass as leverage. Every metre feels like a mile. My arms burn. I reach the top of the hill and look down.

What is that? Looks like someone lying in the knee-high grass. Is that? No no no no no. It can't be! It just can't. Fuck oh fuck oh fuck.

I roll down the hill, ignoring the tear of my belly wound as it stretches open. I land awkwardly, but I keep moving.

Got to keep moving.

Got to get to her.

An eternity passes before I'm at her side, looking down on the lifeless face of the woman I have loved ever since I picked her up on that rainy night thirty years ago.

Her eyes are open, staring upward. Blood saturates her dress, stemming from the single bullet wound in her chest.

I check for a pulse.

Nothing.

She's still warm, so I start CPR, pumping her chest, ignoring the crippling pain in my gut.

– Come on, babe, come back to me.

I check the pulse again – Nothing. Fuck, this can't be happening.

– Come on, baby, don't go! I need you. Don't you leave me!

– Who are you talking to?

I look over my shoulder and see Gabby standing behind me. She's wearing the pink cardigan I bought her for Valentine's Day. She loved.....loves that cardigan.

I look back at the body – still there.

– What's going on? I say, conversing with what can only be a ghost. – Are you an Angel? A ghost?

– How can I be a ghost? You don't believe in life after death. You always said that death was the end of everything – an unfinished sentence. Don't you remember?

– So how come you're here?

– Maybe you've lost your mind.

– Then piss off and leave me alone. I don't have time for hallucinations. I've got to save you. I pump more frantically. One two. Come on, breathe, Gabby! A rib cracks.

– Sounds like you're trying to kill me all over again, Ghost Gabby says.

– I'm saving you!

– But you can't!

– Yes, I can.

– No. You. Can't. Listen to me, Ben / Joe, or whatever your name is. You were an expert on bullet wounds before you met me, right?

– I'm sorry I didn't tell you the truth about me.

– Don't be sorry – just tell me where I'm hit.

– In the upper sternum. The bullet has passed into the chest cavity, most likely cutting the aortic root at the upper left ventricle.

– So, tell me, Mr. Former Assassin – what are my chances of surviving such a wound?

– No chance. This is the work of a professional marksman. You were dead before you even knew you were shot.

– So, with that in mind – can I ask why you're pumping my chest like an idiot?

– Because I can't lose you!

Ghost Gabby kneels by my side, looking me in the eye. – Then how come you already did?

The words hit like a sledgehammer. I touch the body's lifeless face. The skin temperature has dropped. And now I'm in tears, trying to picture her smile, searing it into my memory in case I might forget it. I think about that future we will never have – growing old with our grandchild.

I wrap my arms around her tight and sing to her. – I ain't missing.....you..... I rest my head in the crook of her neck, breathe in her scent, and close my eyes.

Now Ghost Gabby is stern like a headmistress. – What are you doing now? she asks me.

– I'm dying.

– No, you're feeling sorry for yourself.

– What else is there to do?

– And what about Laura, or have you forgotten about her already?

– She's probably dead too.

– But she isn't, is she? You can hear her now – listen!

I cock my ear and hear Laura's voice carried by the wind. She's crying out for help.

– They have her, Ghost Gabby says. – Those evil bastards have our little girl. You know what they'll do to her, don't you? You knew exactly what that man was as soon as you saw him. Are you really going to leave our little girl in the hands of those bastards?

– But I can't help her. My stomach – it hurts so much. I'm so weak – so thirsty.

And then I hear another voice from my past.

– Come on, Pervo, stop being such a useless sap, and get on your feet!

I open my eyes and see Becky standing beside Ghost Gabby. She's got that look on her face, the one she always gave me when I said or did something embarrassing.

– Don't just lie there, she says. – Move your fucking arse!

– You're dead – you can't be here. I let you die.

– Stop crying, you, big girl. Still blaming yourself for everything, I see. It wasn't your fault. You gave me a glimpse of the life I could've had. You can't save everyone, but you can save your daughter.

I picture Laura as a little girl. Always smiling and happy, riding her little tricycle around the garden like a maniac. The thought of her with those men gives me a renewed sense of purpose. I've got to save her.

I try and stand, but the pain is unreal – someone stabbing my genitals with a rusty bread knife. I fall to the floor and scream. Anger and frustration bursts from my lungs.

Now I see Charlotte in front of me, wrapping little Toby in her arms. He's holding Hugo the bear and waving at me. I feel like Luke Skywalker at the end of Return of the Jedi, seeing the ghosts of all the people I've lost.

– It's time to get up, Joey, Charlotte says.

– I can't, it hurts too much.

– You know what you have to do!

– *Yes, you know what you have to do*, another voice says – dark, menacing, and laced with need – the voice that has always scared me.

– I thought you were gone.

– *You'll never get rid of me. I'll always be a part of you – remember?*

– Why have you come back?

– *You know! You asked me to come!*

– I can't let you out. You're a monster!

– Our little girl needs you, Ben. It'll be okay, Ghost Gabby says.

I clench my fists and think about Laura at the mercy of those monsters. I can't abandon my beautiful little girl. I close my eyes and see the key turning. The lock opens, followed by the clatter of a cage and the pitter-patter of excited footsteps running for freedom.

The Hunger

I open my eyes, and I'm alone in the dark. The phantoms of the past are gone. I unwrap myself from Gabriella and kiss her forehead.

Joe would like that.

And then I stand, feeling nothing – no pain, no hatred, no anger – only the sickness and the need to inflict pain. I follow the size twelve footprints leading away from Gabriella's body, driven by voracious hunger, the like of which I have never felt before.

RQ MAGAZINE July 2019,
Issue No. 388.

60 MINUTES WITH CHARLIE QUINNELL – CELEBRITY, STYLE ICON, CONVICTED GANGSTER, MURDERER?? By Sally Jones

I meet Charlie in the bar of the Savoy. He greets me with a warm handshake and a disarming smile, sharply dressed in an impeccably cut Georgio Armani suit. I'm instantly at ease in his company, and it feels as though I'm catching up with an old friend. I have to remind myself that this man has spent the last twenty years locked up in some of Britain's highest security prisons.

So how does it feel to win RQ's author of the year award?

It feels great. When you consider where I was five years ago and where I am now, it's a real honour to receive this award.

You've proved to be quite a controversial figure, often dividing opinion. Can you understand why some might begrudge the success you've had since your release from prison?

Of course, I'm a convicted criminal who has turned his life around. Unfortunately, there are some in society who think crooks should pay for their crimes forever. These people need to get over themselves. I've done my time.

A lot of people think you got off lightly.

Twenty years is 'lightly'?

For multiple murder, twenty years might be seen as light by some people.

Now, that's naughty, Sally. You know I was never convicted of a single murder.

But there has been no shortage of accusations?

What are accusations at the end of the day? Without proof, accusations are just gossip. I can accuse you of falling head over heels in love with me, but that doesn't make it fact until you jump over this table and straddle me.

I'm not quite sure how to follow that.

You're a professional, I'm sure you'll think of something.

It could be argued that the prosecution's failure to secure a murder conviction could be blamed on the unexplained disappearance of key witnesses before the trial. What would you say to that?

I hope you're not implying that I was somehow involved. Such a theory would be predicated on members of the police leaking confidential witness information. Now you can say what you want about me, but I won't hear a word against our magnificent boys in blue. They do a marvellous job.

Do I detect a note of sarcasm?

Of course not.

Did you see that Janet Willis is campaigning for another investigation into the disappearance of her husband? What do you think of that?

I hope she finds him. I think it's a tragedy when a husband leaves his wife.

There are rumours that the police are considering reopening the murder inquiry. Would that worry you?

Why should it? I have nothing to hide. Boris Porter was one of my closest friends. He was like my own flesh and blood. I could never hurt him. As I said before, I hope Janet finds him.

How about the victims of the crimes for which you were convicted? The girls you forced into prostitution, the families you destroyed with your loan sharking activities, the beatings, and the kneecappings – how do you feel about them?

This interview is much tougher than I expected. I thought you'd just ask the name of my tailor and what aftershave I wear.

Like you said, I'm a professional.

Touché. Look, I know I'm not perfect. I've hurt a lot of people. I'm not proud of the things I've done. I'm ashamed.

Wouldn't you say that releasing this book says something to the contrary?

What else should I do? I have to earn a living somehow. Can you see me working at McDonald's? The criminal life is all I've known. I either write about it or I go back to it.

Some attribute the success of your book, 'Running with the Devil' to the chapters which focus on the Ashenridge monastery murders, a mystery that has baffled police for the last twenty-five years. You claim to know the identity of the vigilante responsible for bringing the Webrich child killers to justice. You name the killer as your brother in law, Joe Myers.

Yes, although he liked to think of me as an actual brother, related by blood. He'd want to correct you on that.

The medical examiner who examined the body of Tobias Webrich has gone on record, saying that he had never seen such brutal and sustained torture. Senior police officials investigating the case said they actually felt sorry for Webrich.

That's quite impressive considering he was responsible for the deaths of more than one hundred teenage children and former police detective, Jack Travis. Do you believe your 'brother' could be capable of such violence?

Yes, I do. When we were twelve years old, two older boys wanted to give us a pasting, but Joe had other ideas. He tore them to bits, went through them like they weren't there.

That wasn't in the book?

Yeah, you got yourself an exclusive right there. Back at school, I took him to one side and asked how he'd done it. How did he systematically dismantle two kids twice his size? Then he shrugged like it was nothing. You see, Joe didn't need to take boxing or karate lessons to be tough; he just looked at the human body and knew exactly which buttons to push.

But when you turned sixteen, he disappeared for several years. Where did he go?

I don't know, and I'm not sure I want to. He just vanished. Then a few years later, he randomly walks into my Soho office asking for a job.

What was he like?

He was completely different - everyone was afraid of him, especially my criminal competitors. He would do things other gangsters wouldn't. Word of that spread, and so did my influence. I was running with the Devil, so that meant everybody wanted to be with me, not against me.

If Joe Myers was as bad as you say, why did he care about the murder of teenage prostitutes?

Because he changed.

What could make a man like that change?

He fell in love with my sister, Charlotte.

She must've been quite a woman.

She was. Joe was devastated when she died.

What became of him?

I don't know. He vanished after the murders, and I never heard from him again.

Do you think he may have fallen back into his old ways?

No, because the nuclear fallout would still be settling. But if that ever happens, please give me a heads up so I can book myself a one-way ticket to the moon.

CATFORD, SOUTH LONDON. 1989.

Darkness.

Absolute darkness all around me. I can't believe this is how I'm goin to die. I call out for Mum, but I know there ain't no point. She ain't got no ead so she can't ear nothin no more. Benny's dead too. I know it deep inside.

It's gettin ard to breathe now. The air tastes bad. Eyes are gettin eavy. I'm actually welcomin the end now – anythin to take the pain from my broken body an the fear in my mind.

I close my eyes an say goodbye to the world.

Somewhere above, there are muffled an panicked voices. Maybe they're lookin for me!

– I'm here! Please help me! I try an shout, but it comes out as a whisper. – Please help me!

The voices are movin away now, slippin away like my life.

– Please don't go! Please don't go!

Now I ear shoutin an choppin sounds above me.

– I'm here, I say again.

The choppin gets louder.

They're comin for me. I just got to stay awake.

Metal hits wood. The sound rings in my ears an brings me back to the real world.

Wood splinters. I suck in crisp November air.

A voice speaks in my ear, tellin me everythin's gonna be okay. My vision clears. I see a face – some soppy bloke lookin down at me like I'm Bambi lost in the snow.

– You'll be okay, he says to me, sympathy drippin from his lips as he places the oxygen mask over my face.

– My bruvva, I say, tearin it away. – Is he dead?

– Don't worry about anything, The Sympathetic Man says, as I'm lifted onto a stretcher.

I snarl at him, grabbin his hi-viz jacket. – Tell me! Where is my bruvva?

– Your brother's alive, but he's taken a bad knock to the head. They've taken him to hospital.

– Is he goin to be okay?

– I don't know, but he's in the best possible place.

The Sympathetic Man replaces the oxygen mask an pushes me back on the stretcher. I tilt my head, so I can look back at the hole dug in the garden.

The coffin door hangs open like an ungry mouth.

Five, I fink to myself.

Clay

I kneel beside Danny's body, strokin his fluffy air. I can't believe he's gone. Now it's just me an that orrible cunt, Spivey.

– One down, one to go, Danny! I say to im. – I got one a' them bitches for you. She almost blew my ead off, but I got er. Don't you worry about nothin – we'll get the other ore too. Spivey's out there lookin for er now. He's gonna bring er back ere an then she's gonna pay for what she done to you an Benny.

I ear a car pull up outside, so I look out the window. Spivey sits behind the wheel of a red Mercedes lookin very pleased with imself.

– Please tell me you got er, I say, steppin out the front door.

– I'm offended you have to ask, he replies with a smile. – She's a feisty bitch, that one. I had to put her in the boot.

– Where did ya get the motor?

– Some poor sap stupid enough to pull over when she flagged him down on the road.

Spivey opens the boot an Laura leaps out like a jack in the box, clawin at my face. I grab er wrists, forcin er back down, so she's restin on the mangled remains of what I assume used to be a Good Samaritan. Spivey has sure done a number on the poor cunt. He must've been stabbed fifty times.

Laura frashes like a wild animal, tryin to bite my fingers.

– Fuckin stop that, I say. – Or I'll break your face.

– Let me go, you prick! she screams. – Somebody help!

– You already tried that an you got some poor sod killed, but go on, scream if that's what you wanna do! It ain't gonna do you no good. No one's cummin to rescue you.

She screams as we drag er into the ouse an tie er ands an feet with duct tape.

– You want me to cut out her tongue? Spivey offers.

– No, I say. – She can't beg if she ain't got no tongue an I wanna ear er beg. I look er in the eye. – I wanna know if you'll be as tough as your bitch-whore mother when it's your turn to die.

– You're lying! she says, tears formin in er eyes.

– I don't lie, so you should believe me when I tell you she died well. She almost blew my arm off. I point to the buckshot wound in my upper arm – blood has soaked into my overcoat, drippin from the tips a' my fingers.

– Too bad she missed your face – it would've been an improvement.

– Lets see if you're this lippy when I'm shovellin dirt into that mouth a' yours.

– You want to do it now? Spivey asks.

– We'll bury Danny n Benny first, I say.

– That'll take ages.

– What else would you suggest? We should just leave em to rot – that it?

He don't look appy, but I don't give a fuck – the psychotic little shite'll do as his told or I'll rip his throat out.

– Alright, he sighs. – Just let me take a shit first.

– Now that will take fuckin ages, I say as he eads up the stairs.

Takin a shit for Spivey wasn't an essential action, it was a cherished experience, which should be eked out to last as long as possible. He can sit on the shitter for hours, usin the time to catch up on readin – scrollin away on his mobile. He was even doin that when we was in Iraq, disappearin into the desert – readin porn mags, golfin magazines or any old shit he could lay his ands on.

He's been gone for about fifteen minutes when I ear the unmistakable thud of a body hittin the floor above.

What the fuck was that? Has the dumb cunt ad an eart attack on the shitter or sumfin? I listen for movement, but there is nothin.

No footsteps.

No noise a' any kind. Old country ouses like this usually creaked, but there was none a' that. It's completely still – as if the ouse itself is tryin to be silent, fearful a' disturbin some malevolent presence.

Even the wind outside has stopped.

I call out Spivey's name but get no response.

– Spivey, you, dumb cunt – answer me!

Silence.

I move to the bottom of the stairs an look up the stairwell. – Spivey, can you ear me, you fuckin retard? You better not be playin some silly joke or I'm gonna put you in a fuckin wheelchair!

I pull out my Beretta an cock the ammer – there's sumfin reassurin about the click.

Scalin the stairs slowly, I listen for sound, but there ain't nothin.

When I reach the landin, I'm half expectin someone to rush out of a bedroom, lunging at me like Norman Bate's mum, but no attack comes – just more fuckin silence.

I sneak toward the bathroom. Floorboards creak with every step. I'm not sure what I'm expectin to see when I push open the bathroom door but I'm fearin the worst.

I steady myself an try the andle.

The door creaks open.

Nope, there ain't no Spivey – just a sink, a khazi an a shower.

What the fuck?

I call Spivey's name again. My voice rattles around the house.

Silence replies.

I move back down the allway, drawn toward the nearest bedroom. A faint wheezin comes from behind the door – someone strugglin for breath. Has the dumb cunt had an asthma attack or sumfin? I open the door slowly. The wheezin gets louder. It seems to be cummin from the other side of the bed.

I move to the side to get a better look.

– Jesus Christ! I say out loud, but he didn't have no and in creatin the ideous fing that's slowly leakin into the carpet.

The fing I'd once known as Nicholas Spivey.

Not that he was dead. Nah, he was in that place you don't ever wanna be – that limbo land where you woznt dead, but you wished you was. FUBAR BUNDY was what we called it in the forces. Fucked up beyond all repair but unfortunately not dead yet. One time we'd been out on patrol an Private Ricky Danielson had trod on an IED, blowin himself t' bits.

It took almost ten minutes for im to die. I couldn't believe that. There was barely anythin left of him but somehow, he managed to cling to life. Spivey told me later that he'd found it funny watchin im die – but I bet you anythin, Spivey would swap places with Danielson in a eartbeat right now.

I ave no idea how Spivey's still alive or who or what did this to im, but I ain't ever seen injuries like this before. His body is a mess of exposed veins an nerves. Flaps a' loose skin hang from limbs like the last shreds of paper on a toilet roll. Somehow, the attacker managed to stem any significant blood loss whilst paralysin im. He could probly live like this for hours.

Unlucky brother.

Spivey stares at me with lidless eyes – bulgin in their sockets, ligaments twitchin as they move side to side. He's pleadin – probly wants me to kill im an I don't blame im.

– I'm sorry old friend, I say to im. – But I was never one to ruin another artist's work.

I leave the bedroom, sidesteppin Spivey's tongue, torn out at the root, an artistically placed at the foot of the bed.

Out in the allway, I fink what to do. I didn't see no knife wounds – the attacker must've done that with his bare ands. Spivey may a' been an arsehole an the most sadistic a' sadistic fucks, but I'd trained im to be an ard cunt. How could someone do that to im with their bare ands, wivout makin a single sound? I didn't even ear a floorboard creak.

My eart beats in my chest. What is this unusual feeling? Excitement or fear – I can't tell – it's been so long since I've felt anythin.

I ead downstairs, march up to Laura an aim my Beretta at er ead. – Is there sumfin you wanna tell me? I say to er.

She looks confused. – What do you mean?

– Someone just killed my friend an I want you to tell me who that is!

– I don't know what you're talking about.

I press the muzzle to er forehead, cockin the ammer loud so she can ear it. – Don't you fuckin lie to me!

– I swear I don't...

– I'm gonna blow your fuckin ead off right now!

A door creaks open upstairs an footsteps follow – loud an pronounced like the person responsible is tryin to be eard.

They reach the top of the stairs.... now they're on the stairs – takin each step slowly.

Stomp an Clomp.

Stomp an Clomp.

Stomp an Clomp.

It's like they're pausin for dramatic effect. My eart is pumpin now. I move toward the stairs.

Stomp an Clomp.

Stomp an Clomp.

Stomp an Clomp.

I swing around an aim my Beretta up an empty staircase. What the fuck?

A door slams downstairs in the livin room, which almost makes me jump out a' my skin, an now I'm furious with myself for bein such a pussy.

A whirrin sound comes from the kitchen.

I go to the kitchen an switch off the blender. How the fuck are they doin this? How can they be on the stairs one moment an then be in another room on the other side of the house the next? Can they walk through walls? Maybe there's more than one a' them. I'm startin to feel like I'm bein made to look a right cunt.

– What's going on? Laura asks when I walk back into the livin room. She looks scared.

– Someone's tryin to play games with me, I say. – But they ain't got no idea who they're fuckin with.

I fink about Spivey an ow his gun'd still been tucked into his jeans when I found im. Why didn't they take it? Obviously, this bastard likes to use his ands. Well that fuckin suits me. There ain't a man alive who can take me one on one in a fight.

– We're not on the water, I say out loud. – So, this cat an mouse shit dunnt float! I eject the magazine from my Beretta. – You ear that? That's me emptyin my piece. An there goes the one from the chamber. I'm unarmed now, so why dunnt we dispense with the games?

There is movement behind me – a shufflin from the closet under the stairs.

Then the closet door creaks open.

Laura

The cellar door opens, and something stirs in the darkness. Something feels wrong. Hairs stand on my neck.

Then something emerges from the black – something spat from the depths of Hell. It looks like Dad, but it isn't Dad – there's no warmth or recognition when it looks at me. Its face is alabaster white with skin stretched across razor cheekbones.

The lower half of its body looks like it has been dipped in blood. How is it even standing? It should be dead. I look at Clay, and he does not like what he sees. Terror grips him as the creature steps into the room with effeminate grace. It scans the living room with wonder, as though it'd never seen anything like it before.

The creature turns its gaze on Clay – a gaze of desperate yearning. This thing wants something. Needs it. And it isn't anything good.

Clay backs away as though fearful it might give him some terrible, contagious disease. I doubt Clay has taken a backward step from anyone or anything his entire life. He's probably seen men and women with limbs hacked off, eyes gouged from bloody sockets, but this creature was different – this thing was alive in some abnormal way he'd never faced before.

A current of dread jolts through me, and unbelievably I'm thankful that Clay stands between me and this monster masquerading in Dad's skin.

The creature steps toward Clay and grins. This time Clay holds his ground – fight overcoming the base instinct to flee.

He drops his dice to the floor by his side. They land face up at two and three, but for some inexplicable reason, he utters the word. – Six!

Then he marches toward the creature with fists raised.

I was once married to a girl named Mary.
Who left me, and married a fairy.
I should have told her how much she meant to me.
But I guess some things just aren't meant to be.
I love her and my girls so much.
I suppose I've always been out of touch.
Please know I tried to do the right thing.
But if you're reading this then I've felt the sting.
I hope one day you can be proud of me.
That would make me happy as can be.
I am so glad you found Ray and he makes you
happy, my beautiful Mary.
Even though he's clearly a fairy.

Yours ever faithfully,

Jack xxx

Clay

I smash into the wall then sag to the floor.

The old man picked me up an threw me across the room like I was a tennis ball.

It weren't possible. How could he do that? The old cunt should be dead, lyin in a ditch somewhere, not tossin me about like a fuckin rag doll.

But this weren't the same man I'd left at the cottage – it dinnt move like im – dinnt smell like im – an it certainly dinnt act like im.

This was sumfin else. Sumfin not right – an evil double – a doppelganger – a demon risen from the depths of ell. I get to my feet an smack it across the face. The jawbone cracks an dislocates, juttin out at the side, distendin cheek flesh, pushin bone against taught skin.

I hit it again – harder this time – sumfin pops in its neck. Now its head is bent at a freakish angle. It seems completely unconcerned that its neck is broken.

It don't even blink.

A sick smile splits its face as it slowly rotates its jaw, slidin the mandible bone back into alignment. Next, it jerks its head from side to side. There is a sickenin crunch as the ead snaps straight.

What the fuuu....that ain't possible!

It advances an grips me by the throat, pinnin me against the wall. Pincer-like fingers squeeze my Adam's apple. Fingernails tear into my flesh.

– Get the fuck off me, you, ugly c –

I jam my thumb into its right eye, but it dunnt scream – it just calmly reaches for my and, rippin it away wiv a violent movement.

Pain tears fru my and an now I'm starin at two ragged stumps where my ring an little finger ad been.

Ow the fuck? This can't be appenin.

Now it laughs – an orrible ear piercin cackle that could peel paint off walls.

It lifts my shirt, exposin bare flesh.

– I wonder what we have here, The Doppelganger says. The voice is cold an unfeelin, but somehow childish an effeminate. – Let's see what we can find if we reach deep inside.

Fingers slide underneath the skin a' my stomach – twistin, probin an explorin – diggin deeper – violatin my body.

I want to scream, but I'm frozen – transported back to that night when I'd found The Ghoul on top of Benny in his bed – when he'd pinned me down an run that flame across my naked skin.

I'd been so fuckin elpless. And now the same fing was appenin ere! I promised myself when I came out a' that grave that I'd never be that elpless again.

The Ghoul's words echo in my mind. – *You really shouldn't make promises you can't keep. A man should always keep his word – you remember that.*

Well fuck The Ghoul an fuck this freak!

I reach for my knife, tucked behind my back – slidin it from its sheath, slashin across The Doppleganger's inner elbow joint – severin ligaments controllin the forearm.

It releases its grip an I land on the floor wiv a bump. The wounds in my stomach burn. I jump to my feet an make precise cuts fru its bicep an Trapezius muscle.

Now The Doppelganger's left arm hangs limply by its side, like a puppet with a cut string. It stares in bewilderment at the ruined limb – dunnt this fing feel pain?

I frust my blade into the creature's stomach, twistin until it sinks to its knees. Now I'm on top of it, poundin its ead into the floor – the cheekbone an eye socket cave in – its breath comes in orrid mechanical rasps.

– This is what you get when you fuck with me! I shout, slammin my fist into its face again. – You ear me, ya fuckin cunt?

But it ain't payin me no attention – it just stares at Laura wiv a dumb look on its face.

Laura

Oh, my God! That's really him. He's really in there!

I'd recognise that wink anywhere. One half of his face may have collapsed but still – only Dad could mess up a wink so badly.

Clay readies another punch.

– Please! I scream at the top of my lungs, struggling against my restraints. – Please, stop hurting my Dad!

Clay looks up and smiles. – You want this to end?

Tears leak from my eyes. I feel so weak and broken. – I want all of this to end. I can't take this anymore!

– Don't worry, Laura, once I deal with this freak – we can get you in the ground.

Clay climbs off Dad and retrieves his gun – reloading clumsily with his damaged hand.

– Please stop this!

– Sssssh, he says, forefinger across his lips. – You've got your whole life behind ya now!

He aims at Dad's head.

– Please don't kill my dad!

– I don't know what this fing is, but it ain't your dad! It shouldn't feel bad tho – after all, there ain't no man that can take me in a fight.

Now Dad speaks in a terrible, high-pitched voice. – What makes you think I'm a man. I'm not a man! Dad's arm shoots up, fingers clenching Clay's crotch. – And guess what.... neither are you!

There is a loud pop, and I'm pretty sure I hear testicles explode. Clay lets out a harrowing, ear-splitting scream cut short when Dad tears his throat out.

Jobe

What happened? Where am I?

My vision is badly blurred. My whole body hurts – slowly shutting down.

Laura looks down on me. She looks so upset. – Dad, please don't leave me!

– Are you safe, Laura? Where are those men?

– They're all dead. You saved me!

I turn my head and see the man who'd shot me at Margaret's. He's lying face down with his oesophagus hanging out. Blood pools around his body.

– So, you got them all then, you scary bitch? Thank you, my old friend!

The Hunger does not reply – it is truly gone now.

I stroke tears from Laura's face. – I'm very sorry about this my little munchkin, but I'm going to die now.

– No, you can't – you can't leave me! You're going to be okay – we're going to get you some help and you'll be okay.

– It's okay, darling. I'm going to be with your mother.

– No, please don't go! Please don't go!

I wish I could stay with her – be with her when she gives birth to her baby. I know she'll be a fantastic mother. I'm so proud of her – my beautiful, intelligent daughter.

She kisses my forehead. – Please, Dad, I love you and Mum. I don't want you to go.

– I love you too, I say, closing my eyes.

Her voice is further away now. Everything is getting darker. Warmth passes through me. Is this it? The end.

I hope there's an afterlife, and Gabby is waiting for me on the other side. I pray I will get to see her smile again.

It would be good to see Charlotte, although that could be a little awkward. How does Heaven work for those people who have lost a partner and found someone new – they don't offer guidance on that in the Bible, do they? Maybe it's some kind of sexual free-for-all where jealousy and envy don't exist.

I wonder if Toby is all grown up – I hope he has forgiven me.

And now I think about Becky – my beautiful friend. I owe her so much. She taught me how to live again. She taught me how to love and

There is an old illusion
It is called good and evil.
　　　　-FRIEDRICH NIETZSCHE.

Printed in Great Britain
by Amazon